She looked down at his hand. 'You said you weren't going to touch me again.'

'I'm. . .I'm sorry.' But Patrick's hand stayed, refusing his will, and the other stole up to match it on her shoulder.

'Honestly, Claire, what do you take me for?'

'A lion.' She didn't try and free herself, but steadily held the blue, blue eyes. 'Trapped here by your lion's pride.'

'Maybe,' he admitted. 'I certainly couldn't live with myself if I left you two—but that's the least of it.' He kept his hands on her shoulders, his eyes fixing hers. 'I'm not going to kiss you, I'm not, I'm not. . .'

And he did, so gently and undemandingly that she just had to kiss him back, to show it was all right.

We hope that you're enjoying our new addition to our Contemporary Romance series—stories which take a light-hearted look at the Zodiac and show that love can be written in the stars!

Every month you can get to know a different combination of star-crossed lovers, with one story that follows the fortunes of a hero or heroine when they embark on the romance of a lifetime with somebody born under another sign of the Zodiac. This month features a sizzling love-affair between **Leo** and **Sagittarius**.

To find out more fascinating facts about this month's featured star-sign, turn to the back pages of this book . . .

ABOUT THIS MONTH'S AUTHOR

Jessica Marchant says: 'The ancient wisdom of Astrology shows patterns in everything, from the movements of shadows to the movements of stars. Those patterns have worked well for me. While I feel horoscopes can tell me something, I always bow to the superior wisdom of Love. A fiery Sagittarian, I married a level-headed Libran, and we are still living happily ever after.'

THE TRAGANA FLAME

BY

JESSICA MARCHANT

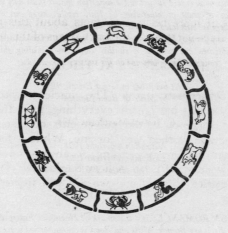

MILLS & BOON LIMITED
ETON HOUSE   18–24 PARADISE ROAD
RICHMOND   SURREY   TW9 1SR

*First published in Great Britain 1991
by Mills & Boon Limited*

© Jessica Marchant 1991

*Australian copyright 1991
Philippine copyright 1991
This edition 1991*

ISBN 0 263 77166 0

STARSIGN ROMANCES is a trademark of Harlequin Enterprises B.V., Fribourg Branch. Mills and Boon is an authorised user.

*Set in 10 on 11 pt Linotron Baskerville
01-9107-56647 Z
Typeset in Great Britain by Centracet, Cambridge
Made and printed in Great Britain*

CHAPTER ONE

'DONNA?' The tall silhouette at the other end of the corridor started joyfully forwards.

Claire froze, but only for a moment. Then she blew out her candle, set its wax-dripping silver holder on the walnut side-table, and snatched up the rifle which she had laid there ready.

So I was right, a distant part of her mind argued, satisfied because she could meet this danger properly prepared.

It showed she was coping. Wakened by Al, she had decided to stay up, put on her toughest jeans and battledress-blouson, loop her black hair in its double pony-tail, and go for another scout around this part of the monastery to make sure that all was well. All was *not* well, but now she trusted herself to cope with that, too.

She couldn't see what manner of man he was, this invader of her month-long loneliness and two-day solitude. He was nothing but a huge shadow and a deep voice, stealthy yet passionate with the delight of having found his Donna. But he hadn't; if his Donna had ever been here she must have gone with the others two days ago. And beyond the high double doorway which framed him, the brilliant oblongs of the refectory windows showed the city of Tragana burning. Even through those closed windows you could smell the acrid smoke as it drifted across the river.

'Burning and worse,' she murmured to herself, facing it at last.

The occasional distant crash might be a building giving way. But the other noises—those rattling cracks which broke out every now and again—they could only be gunfire answered by more gunfire. Something bad was happening over there, and now she must be ready for anything.

'Donna?'

This time he followed the name with a flood of words which Claire didn't understand. Once more she had to fight the feeling that he had come here, not to pillage and burn and slaughter, but to help. He must be some local lover, determined to reach his girl and get her across the river and away from here to safety. For the umpteenth time Claire wished she'd studied languages instead of art history, and so could understand what he was saying.

But if I'd done languages, I wouldn't be here, she reminded herself. And Al wouldn't have anybody.

The thought stiffened her courage, and put a commanding edge on her voice. 'Hands up!' If he didn't understand English, he must at least hear from her tone that she meant business. 'Or I fire.'

Now it was his turn to freeze. He remained a featureless blackness, but when he spoke again the passion had drained from his voice, leaving it cool, dry, almost amused.

'Both hands?'

'Of course both hands,' she retorted, thrown more than she dared show by his complete confidence and perfect English.

'Very well.' Enigmatic against the flame-lit refectory, he raised arms which in outline seemed frighteningly muscular. 'And remember, it's what you told me to do.'

'Now walk back there.' She gestured with a movement of her head to the bright-lit space beyond him—the great room which he had sprung from.

'Is that wise?' His meaning was clear as the noise of

some vile automatic weapon stuttered across the water.
'They're shooting.'

'Not in this direction. We haven't lost so much as a
window. . .'

'We?'

Claire bit her lip. It was always going to be 'we' from
now on, she was sure of that. She'd never desert Al. If
anyone tried to harm him, they'd have to take her first.
But she should never have even hinted at his presence,
and, anyway, why was she talking of Tragana Monastery
as if she owned it? Nobody owned it or had the right to.
Its beauty belonged to the whole world.

'Stop arguing——' she slanted the rifle a little so that
the silver-worked handle glittered in the bronze light
'—and move!'

'Ma'am.' The silhouette turned, and sauntered back
the way it had come.

Claire followed him, rifle at the ready, into the cool,
high space still known as the refectory. At one time the
monks had eaten here, but they and their whole way of
life had been dismissed from this river-island two
hundred years ago. Their austere, scrubbed boards had
long gone, and now a single rosewood banquet-table and
its ranks of attendant chairs gleamed and flickered in the
flame-light from the row of tall windows.

The intruder turned to face her, and Clare almost
dropped the rifle in her confusion. The nearer they'd
approached the coppery light, the more she'd been aware
of how much of him it revealed—strong legs with only a
dusting of hair to shield their leisurely progress; strong
feet padding soundlessly over the marble tiles; strong
shoulders sparkling here and there with bright droplets
which shook free of the soaked, dark mane and lingered
in the dark hair of his chest.

Now she was able to have her first good look at him,

she could no longer ignore what she'd been trying not to see. 'You haven't got anything on!'

'Well, hardly anything.' He placed himself behind the solid back of a chair, arms still raised. 'Who are you telling?'

'You swam the river?'

'I did.' The dark eyes mocked her under heavy brows which lifted at the corners like an eagle's wings. 'And I'm bound to tell you, these trunks aren't made for swimming.' He stepped from behind his sheltering chair. 'If you don't let me do something about them, they'll be——'

'Pull them up,' she ordered hastily.

'Much obliged.'

He dropped his hands—long-fingered hands with broad, capable palms—to his one garment. The boxer-shorts, absurdly patterned in colours that were impossible to make out in the searing glow from across the river, slid up the narrow hips and settled more modestly over the flat belly. The drying hair of his sinewy forearms glittered with what she now knew was river water, as he raised them again in the air.

'The damn things are sliding already.' He glanced down, flame-light rippling on his powerful neck while his black lashes made their own humorous comment on his plight. 'Keeping your hands up kind of pulls in all your muscles——'

'Grab them.' She waited while he anchored the shorts in a businesslike fist. 'I think I've seen enough——'

'I should hope so,' he interrupted with comic primness. 'This is further than I usually go without spotlight and drum-roll.'

'—to know you're not carrying concealed weapons,' she finished, raising her voice to be heard through his flippancy.

'No.' Those lashes swept down and up, letting the

glinting dark eyes stare directly into hers while the long mouth quirked up on one side. 'Definitely no concealed weapons.'

She felt the chased metal of the rifle-butt sticky beneath her palm. What on earth was wrong with her? Was it reaction to the strain of the last two days? Or could it be that the new experience of her love for Al, slowly dawning through the need to care for and comfort him, had opened her to other experiences she might have? Was that why, at this moment, she so desperately envied the absent, mysterious Donna?

'I'd have brought one if I could, but it would only have got wet.' He spoke as if trying to change the subject, which was odd when he was still on weapons. 'And they said everyone had gone from here. Including, I suppose, my best girl.'

'Your best girl,' she repeated, still with that puzzling, envious sense of loss. 'Is she this Donna you were calling for?'

'From a distance, I thought you were her.' He stared at Claire with a distant, abstract desire. 'All that smooth dark hair, and the pale skin. . .' He leaned forward, his urgency having suddenly returned. 'Is anyone here at all?'

'Nobody.' She shook her head. 'Only me and. . .'

She broke off, furious with herself. Yet how could she keep Al out of her talk, when he had become so much a part of her life? And the stranger picked up her blunder at once, just as he had earlier when she'd uttered that careless 'we'.

'You're hiding something.' His breath quickened, every well-defined muscle suddenly tense. 'Did some of them stay, after all?'

'You mean the Secret Police?' she asked, and again that chill of loss settled in her stomach.

So he knew, as she herself hadn't until she arrived,

that they used Tragana as a garrison. The forbidding Secret Police had made this island their fortress, and, besides that, the Danube here was lethally fast. Yet he'd swum the river, and been prepared the brave the sinister armed men who until two days ago had guarded every corner of the monastery; and all for the sake of this unknown Donna.

'Tell me,' he ordered tersely, as if he were the one in command of the rifle. 'Who are you hiding?'

'Nobody.' But she couldn't dismiss Al like that, as if he didn't matter. 'Nobody who could possibly interest you,' she amended, glad to have found a truthful way of putting it.

'Who, for God's sake?' He took a lithe step towards her, his fist tight on his waistband.

'Keep your distance.' She jumped back, and pointed the gun full at his chest. 'This is loaded——'

'Is it hell. I doubt if they make the ammunition any more.'

He took the antique rifle from her with his free hand, and she made no effort to resist. She was glad to be rid of the thing, even if he had made her look silly.

'You knew all along I'd never be able to use it,' she accused, trying to keep her voice steady. 'Why did you pretend to be doing what I told you?'

He shrugged, muscles rippling across the broad shoulders, and regarded her over the gun with that derisive, one-side-only smile. 'It seemed the best way to convince you I'm harmless.'

'Harmless isn't the word I'd have used.'

'Exactly.' He hooked the nearest chair from the table with a powerful foot, and dropped the rifle on to the padded seat. 'Couldn't you find a more up-to-date weapon?'

'I didn't want to hurt anybody.' She saw his smile widen, and hurried to protest. 'All I needed was a way

of frightening off looters. Th-this——' she nodded sideways at the gun '—was hanging in Colonel Danev's
office. I th-think. . .'

Was it moving her head which had caused this new
buzzing in her ears? Or relief at not having to pretend
she might shoot? Or maybe a better, wider relief at the
kind of person he'd turned out to be—one who perhaps
really could help. The buzz grew to a roar, and she
couldn't see properly any more, but she doggedly finished what she was trying to tell him.

'I think his great-grandfather used it in the Balkan
Wars.'

'And it was old then. . . Here!'

'I'm all right.'

But she wasn't. The fear and worry and loneliness,
not just of the last two days but of the whole dreadful
month that she'd been here, were taking their toll at last.
The leaping flames, the copper-glowing table, the high,
red-tinged ceiling and the useless, red-sparkling chandeliers had all whirled into one gigantic fiery wheel, and
she no longer knew up from down or left from right.

And his hands were only making it worse, supporting
so gently either side of her waist. They positively invited
her to give in, to sway forwards and rest her head on
that broad, dark-haired chest. . .

'I'm all right!' She sprang back as if he'd burnt her.
'Just leave me alone.'

'Come on, let's get you sitting down.'

And then he'd freed another chair from the table, and
pushed her gently into it. Only when she felt its padded
seat give to her weight, its tooled leather support her
back, did she realise how near she'd been to collapse.
She kept her head lowered, and laced her hands in her
lap to stop them betraying her.

'I'm all right, really. It's just. . .'

She glanced out to the orange-lit skyline across the

river. All day she had been trying to tell herself that it wasn't happening, and even now, to judge by what she could see from here, the houses and towers and domed churches of the old city seemed undamaged. Behind them, though, on one of the outlying hills, the flames mounted cloud-high, and sparks shot higher still into the invisible pall which must be smoke blacking out the stars.

'Wh-what's going on?' she asked, limp with the relief of at last being able to discuss it. 'What's it all about?'

'It's the government buildings on Volpes hill.' He turned to survey the fires, which were indeed confined to the ugly, blank boxes dominating the town from the west. 'They did it with petrol bombs.'

'Wh-who did?'

'Students, mostly.' He pushed the rifle to the back of the other chair, and sank beside her. 'Look, you're the girl who won this year's Cortesi Scholarship, aren't you? Claire. . .' A moment's pause and he had it. 'Claire Fletcher.'

She jumped, the sound of her own name too much for her worn nerves. 'How did you know?'

'It's my job to know.'

His forearm, each hair erect as a tiny high-tension wire, moved to where his breast-pocket would have been if he'd had one. When he realised the mistake he shrugged and grinned. She stared helplessly at what the shrug did to the broad shoulders, then tore her gaze away and concentrated on his face.

I like that grin, she decided, as she tried to gather in her scattered thoughts. It helps.

It still went mockingly up on one side, deepening the groove between cheekbone and jaw. But it showed beautiful, even teeth, and the mockery was all against himself.

'I seem to have left my cards in my other suit.'

'Fancy.' She felt better already at the tiny joke. 'Perhaps you could tell me who you are by word of mouth?'

Oh, dear, why had she put it like that? Now she couldn't stop looking at his mouth—the long upper lip rising on one side, the full lower lip hinting at that passion which had been so clear in his voice a few minutes ago.

'Patrick Donovan. Vice-Consul, British Embassy.'

'So that's why your English is so good.'

'Not bad, is it?' he observed ironically. 'For a Scot.'

'Are you?' Now he'd told her, she could hear it; a tiny emphasis of the 'r', a tiny extra depth to the 'o'. 'Your name's Irish.'

He sketched a brief, courtly bow. 'My apologies.'

'Don't be like that.' She closed her eyes and shook her head, desperate to regain her courage. 'I only meant——'

'Cheer up.' He reached forward and patted her shoulder. 'My great-grandfather settled in Scotland, that's all,' he explained, to make up for his sarcasm. 'The place is full of Irishmen.'

She moved her shoulder under his hand. When she'd first felt it she'd been glad of the contact, something to depend on in the worries of the last two days; but now she wasn't so sure. The touch had flared through the thick cotton of her blouson to a heat that melted her like candle-wax. Already she could feel the unwelcome rays of it, spreading down her spine and up her scalp and leaving in its wake a weakness which she couldn't afford.

She gazed at him imploringly, and perhaps he understood. Yet when he drew back, when his hand dropped sedately to his sinewy thigh, the chill was almost unbearable. To distract herself from it, she drew the discarded gun from between him and the chair-back, and laid it across her lap.

'How on earth does it come to be your job to know about me?'

'The first British citizen to have won the Cortesi Scholarship?' The eagle's-wing eyebrows rose in gentle query. 'Of course we know about you.'

She remembered her brief journey through the capital on her arrival a month ago. She'd been taken in a blacked-out limousine from the airport to the palace which had once been royal, and led through a maze of corridors, all bristling with armed guards, to a tapestried state apartment where a tiny, dried-up man had shaken her hand. A few translated words of greeting from him, and of gratitude from her, and she'd been free to hasten thankfully to Tragana and the magnificent frescoes which she had chosen to study.

'It's nothing to do with the British government. Mr Cortesi's paying. . . *was* paying,' she corrected herself, wondering if anything had happened to that little yellow stick of an old man.

'Cortesi pays for nothing. He takes what he wants.' Patrick Donovan looked round him at the gold-framed oil-paintings, the high, white and gold doors, the gilded, priceless cupboards and side-tables. 'Same as he took this place from the Malinesi family.'

'Who themselves took it from the monks, two hundred years ago,' she reminded him. 'If the embassy's that interested in me, why haven't I heard anything from you? I've been here a month.'

'That long, and you haven't noticed the Forget-me-nots? The Secret Police,' he added, seeing her bewilderment. 'Those guys in the bright blue caps. That's why they call them——'

'Forget-me-nots.' She shuddered at the sinister exactness of the name. 'I didn't know the nickname, but I know *them*. They've been everywhere, ever since my plane landed.'

Especially here. In the garden, they had patrolled the whole length of the walls. Outside the door of her room, a guard had stood with bayonet fixed night and day. In the library she couldn't draw a book from a shelf without passing one, and even in the church they'd been scattered about the arches like a miserable modern comment on the timeless beauty of the frescoes.

'Which is why we haven't been in touch.' Patrick Donovan called her back to the present as from a nightmare.

'And wouldn't be now, I suppose,' she murmured, trying to collect her scattered thoughts, 'if it weren't for your Donna.'

'She was never my Donna.' The long mouth hardened, the dark eyes pools of shadow in the uncertain light. 'Even if old Cortesi would have allowed it——'

'Cortesi?' She sat up sharply as she heard him speak again of the aged dictator. 'What has he to do with it?'

'Never mind. I really didn't drive here because of Donna.'

Oh, no? she thought disbelievingly, and felt another rush of envy for the unknown woman who could provoke such a man to such feats.

'So you drove here?' she asked aloud. 'Before you could swim rivers and storm fortresses in nothing but your trunks, you had to drive a hundred miles?'

'It wasn't so bad.' Again he lifted those shoulders in that disturbing shrug. 'The roads are quiet, and we needed to know what's going on down here.'

'And what is?'

'A peaceful protest——'

'*Peaceful*!' she echoed, against another volley of shots.

'It started out peaceful. Students.' He nodded across the river to where the university buildings rose from their own eastern hill, their apparently intact glass walls winking in the flamelight. 'Then the townspeople joined in, and Cortesi set the army on them.'

'Oh, God.' She buried her head in her hands, ashamed of having accepted the hospitality of such a ruler.

'It isn't as bad as it sounds.' He must have seen her distress and be offering a shred of comfort, but as he went on his voice flared with excitement. 'I gather the soldiers wouldn't play. The Forget-me-nots had to call in reinforcements.'

'So that's where they've all gone from here?'

'Those blue-capped bastards have everything to lose if Cortesi falls. They'll fight to the last man—how many,' he demanded urgently, 'd'you think they'd get from here?'

'I don't know.' She raised her head and shook it, weakened again by her memory of the past month. 'Nobody told me anything. Nobody talked to me at all. It was almost a relief to wake up yesterday. . .' She glanced at a gold and lapis lazuli clock, and amended her last word. 'I mean, the day before yesterday, and find they'd all gone.'

Her thick-walled room was on the other side of the building, near the kitchens, in the corridor which had once housed the lay-brothers. She'd been instructed always to wait there for meals, so that morning she'd waited and waited for the silent Mara to bring breakfast. Only hunger had driven her at last to the cavernous kitchens to see what the trouble was.

'It was like the *Mary Celeste*,' she said, able at last to face the enormity of it. 'Eggs half whisked on the table. A bucket and mop on the floor. Milk burnt over.'

'And no Forget-me-nots?'

She shook her head. It had taken all her courage to walk to the barracks at the far end of the monastery. She'd only gone there after she'd found Al and needed to be sure that the place was empty of anyone who could either help or hurt him. And it was. The Secret Police—those menacing, blue-capped guards who had so poisoned her time here—had left in disorder.

'They'd thrown clothes everywhere,' she told her companion, 'as if they'd had to pack in a hurry.'

'But they took all their weapons?'

'I suppose so. I didn't see any except this one.' She glanced down at the historic rifle in her lap. 'Some of them had been halfway through a card-game.' She recalled the scattered coins and scraps of pasteboard. 'And they must have set breakfast the night before, but they hadn't eaten it; you could feed an army——' She broke off with a sinking in her stomach. 'So they're over there, fighting the army. Isn't that civil war?'

'Not exactly; there's too few of them. What it seems to be,' Patrick Donovan exulted, 'is a nation freeing itself——' Now it was his turn to break off, one side of the long mouth rising in that half-smile which this time was an apology. 'I'm not usually that pompous.'

'You weren't pomous,' she breathed, fascinated by the way his nostrils had flared and his dark eyes glowed in the shifting flames. 'Just a typical Leo.'

'A *what?*' He blinked. 'You mean the zodiac sign? But how d'you know I'm a Leo?'

'They think big.'

'So do lots of people. That's about the flimsiest evidence I ever heard of.'

'You are a Leo, though, aren't you?' She glanced down at the drying boxer-shorts. 'I bet somebody gave you those as a present.'

'The girlfriend before last.' He followed her gaze, raising those disturbing arms to look down at the shorts. 'Are they supposed to prove something?'

'The pattern. All those little signs like a lion's mane.' She looked away, suddenly self-conscious about where she'd been staring. 'That's the Leo symbol.'

'Rubbish. It's just a pattern.'

'All right.' The dismissive tone brought her to her feet before she knew it. 'Come to my cell and see the ones in my cupboard. . .'

She bit her lip in confusion. Had she really invited this mostly-naked man to her room? To show him a pair of *panties*, for goodness' sake? She must be more upset than she knew, to be so carried away by her Sagittarian determination to win an argument.

'They—er—they were all on sale at one of the chain-stores last Christmas,' she muttered rapidly, hoping to talk herself past her gaffe. 'The two wavy lines for Aquarius, the sort of M with a long tail for Scorpio, the arrow. . .'

Hers had the arrow pattern for Sagittarius, but this time she had the sense to stop short. Already he had risen to his feet, and any minute might demand to see what she had mentioned was in her cupboard.

However, she had misjudged him. When he spoke, it was clear that he wanted at least as much as she did to spare either of them further embarrassment and, more-over, had already dismissed her wild chatter of star signs.

'Didn't I hear you say there were clothes all over the barracks?' He indicated the corridor which she had come from, lifted the gun from her as if he were a gentleman relieving a lady of a parasol, and stood back. 'Could you lead me to them?'

'N-not all the way.' But already his easy habit of command had compelled her to the door. 'I'll show you, though, and get you a light.'

She felt an immense relief at being back in the shadows of the corridor. She had enough of a routine going by now to return with a sure step to the side-table, draw her precious matches from her pocket, and relight with-out fuss the candle she had left there.

'Have you any idea what's happened to the power?' she asked, raising the silver candlestick with its little fluttering light.

'It's gone up with the rest, on Volpes. Just as well for me,' he added, padding after her along the cream-walled corridor. 'I doubt whether I'd have made it here if they'd had their usual searchlights on the water.'

'Not to mention their electric fence.'

'That was no problem; they've left the gates open.'

'Fool's luck,' she threw back over her shoulder. 'What on earth you thought you could do here with no clothes on——'

'I had to swim,' he reminded her coolly. 'This isn't the Isle of Wight, with regular ferries.'

'There must have been a boat of some kind.'

'And a fine upstanding target I'd have made if I'd used one.'

'How did you know you weren't going to be shot *here*, the minute you stepped ashore?' she persisted.

'I've told you why.' His growl vibrated down her spine. 'Everybody in Tragana knows the Forget-me-nots have gone from here.'

'The army might have come instead. Or looters,' she added, recalling her chief fear when she'd first seen him.

'They wouldn't; not ordinary people. This island's holy ground.'

'I see.'

And as she set her candle on the huge scrubbed kitchen table, she really did see. The Forget-me-nots weren't ordinary people as he and she understood the term, but the soldiers were. Young conscripts from fields and shops and offices, they shared the beliefs of the families they had left. And those beliefs, she realised, would keep Tragana Monastery safe in this, or any other turmoil. Nobody would desecrate this place of ancient faith.

'Oh, I wish I'd been able to get to know them,' she exclaimed on a wave of frustrated liking for the people who had created her beloved frescoes. 'Have they really a hope of being free after all?'

'After all,' he repeated, teasing out her meaning. 'You've been learning a thing or two since you came here, haven't you?'

She admitted it, shamefaced. 'Back at college, I used to think Cortesi a good man.'

'So did lots of people who should have known better. How did you find him out?'

'Those policemen.' She shuddered. 'And such luxury here, when over there. . .'

But she couldn't speak of that. She'd been kept here like a prisoner, allowed to move only about the narrow confines of the island, and little even of that. The only time she'd crossed the river to the beautiful old city, a heavily armed escort had gone with her, and every minute that she was there she'd felt the misery and hatred of the citizens like knives through a fence. She'd been glad to get back here, to her frescoes and her thesis, and hadn't asked any further permission to go sightseeing.

'You must be glad you found these.' He had taken up another of her candles, in a neat pewter holder, and was now lighting it from the first. 'How have you been managing for food?'

'There's the biggest collection of freezers you ever saw through there.' She waved at the blurred distances beyond the pillars. 'Even in this heat, they'll keep the goodies fresh for a while yet. And that's before you think about cheese and stuff.'

'And fuel?' He glanced at the enormous old kitchen range.

'I've been eating cold.'

'Yet you've lit that? In this heat?'

'It. . .it was something to do. Er—the barracks are this way.' She beckoned him under the low, vaulted roof, between the squat, shadowy pillars, to a far-off door, and gave him the complicated directions for where he must go. 'But watch out at the library; it's the *second* door and it's covered with imitation bookshelves.'

He listened with growing approval. 'You're not just a pretty face, are you, Claire Fletcher?'

'You. . .you won't be long?' For the life of her, she couldn't keep that pleading note from her voice. 'I'll. . . I'll make you a hot drink when you get back.'

'So that's why you lit the stove?' He brought his light closer to her. 'For hot drinks?'

She nodded, unable to speak the lie. For herself she'd have been perfectly happy with the milk and fruit juice which had been left here in such copious supplies. Only Al's needs had kept her struggling with that damned stove until at last she'd got it lit.

'Coffee'd be great,' he told her, and moved off into the shadows.

How strange, she thought, watching the tiny brightness of his candle grow ever smaller in the long, long reaches of the low-arched corridor. Only a few minutes ago I was holding a gun at him, and now I can't wait to have him back with me.

As she had already noticed, the time went quicker when you had someone to work for. She lit two more candles, found an old enamel percolator in a cupboard, and washed the dust off it. The coffee was easily traced by its delicious smell—only the best for any Cortesi establishment—and she'd kept water permanently heating in the great iron kettle. It pleased her to think how Patrick Donovan would return to find these aching, shadowy spaces filled with the friendly aroma of a good breakfast.

And come to that, it was almost breakfast time. She

glanced at the old, weighted wall-clock. If you break-
fasted *very* early.

She wandered to the shining ranks of freezer cabinets
which lined one wall, but didn't open them. The cold in
them must be conserved. She'd wait till he got back, and
ask him if he wanted anything to eat, and then
she'd——

'Claire?'

As before when he'd used her name, she jumped, then
hurried over to him. It was a relief to see him dressed,
but he seemed to have grown bigger than ever in that
dark T-shirt and trousers. He still walked silently,
padding towards her through the gloom like a great
night-hunting cat. She shivered, and scolded herself.

'Lions don't eat people.' She only realised she'd
spoken aloud when he reacted.

'What?' He held the light up to her face. 'Are you all
right? You've been under a lot of strain.'

'I expect it was hearing my name,' she excused herself.
'Nobody's called me that since I left England.'

'So they were very formal here?'

'If they talked to me at all. Colonel Danev—the
commandant,' she interrupted herself to explain, 'he
gave me dinner in the refectory when I first arrived.'

It had been a difficult evening. The harsh brilliance of
the chandeliers had given her a headache, and she'd had
no interest at all in the endless succession of rich dishes.
Through his interpreter, the greying, ramrod-straight
commandant had paid her heavy compliments which
he'd perhaps hoped she'd respond to. However that
might be, he'd presently made no secret of his boredom,
and hadn't asked her again.

She shook herself free of the memory, and copied the
soft, local accent. 'They all called me Mees Fletchair.'

'When you speak like that, you even *sound* like Donna.'

'You must——' She glanced up at him, dismayed

afresh by the reminder. 'You must—er—like her very much?'

'I wouldn't put it quite like that.' He sighed, and led the way to the table. 'Likewise, if I'm honest, I never had much hope of finding her here. The trail's cold.'

'You mean——' she followed him '—you heard she'd come here?'

'You have to go by rumours, in this country.' He set down his candle, and lowered his great length to one of the incongruous plastic chairs which seemed too light for his weight. 'Another student at the academy told me——' He stopped, and sighed again. 'But that was months ago.'

'Long before I arrived, then.' How strange to think what this other girl—his girl—had lived here before her. 'I didn't see or hear anything of her. But then, this place is so enormous,' Claire added with feeling. 'Anything could happen in it.'

And probably had. Her study-bedroom a little way from here, the corridors to the library, the arched cloisters which led to the church, and the garden where you couldn't see the river but only hear it lapping beyond the high, peach-gold walls—those were all she'd come to know of Tragana in the time she'd been here. Until the last two terrifying days, the rest of the building had been closed to her.

'So you heard and saw nothing.' He made it a resigned statement of fact. 'The only surprise about that is Cortesi ever letting you come at all to this island with his Forget-me-nots.'

'That's another thing.' She was so glad to be able to say it at last, and she spoke more forcefully than she meant to. 'Only a very bad man could settle all those. . .those trained killers in Tragana.'

'They're always kept well away from real human beings,' he agreed, this marvellous real human being who had come to her exactly when she needed him most. 'That was part of the strategy.' He stared at her curiously. 'It's quite something to have been caged with that lot for a whole month, and still be. . .what you are.' He looked away quickly. 'Had you nobody to talk to at all?'

'Only Mara, who brought my food, and she wouldn't say much. There was an interpreter.' She tried not to quail at the mere memory of the man's lizard-like eyes and cold, drawling English. 'I—I did without him, where I could. It's been the oddest time.'

'Only odd?' He stared again, the tiny points of candle-flame reflecting like probes from the dark eyes. 'Not scary? Not lonely?'

'Both. Still——' she gave herself a little shake, refusing pity '—the church and the library were worth it. My frescoes——'

'And they were enough for you? Even in the last two days?'

'Oh, that's been quite different. You see, I. . .'

She broke off, wondering how to tell him. He'd have to know some time, and she was sure that, when he did, he'd help. Besides, she longed to talk about Al, and the miracle of finding him, and the way he'd carried her through this awful time just by being here, and being himself. She stared up at this lion-man, this deliverer, this Patrick Donovan, and wondered how to begin.

'You're a brave woman, Claire Fletcher,' he said softly.

And then his hands were strong on her shoulders, his lips firm on her cheek. A lock of his damp hair dropped cool against her temple, and, below it, those eyelashes brushed her like feathers; the wing-feathers of an eagle. . . Before she knew it, she had turned her head and taken his kiss full on the mouth.

'Here!' He drew away in amazement, upright once more in his own chair. 'I didn't mean it like that.'

'Then you should be more careful.' She huddled her arms together. 'I've had nothing here; nothing and nobody until——'

She'd been about to tumble it out, to tell him everything, but had to stop. He rose and drew her up with him into the strong circle of his arms, where nothing would ever frighten her again.

How could she do anything but return his kiss? Especially when she wanted it so much; had wanted it ever since she first saw this passionate mouth. These hard shoulders were hers now, their strength a sure resting place for her hands. She opened her lips, and his tongue took sweet possession of hers, and her fingers moved to the coolness of his river-damp hair. While she clung to him like this she could forget everything. Nothing mattered but herself and Al and him—three together in a world open to none but them, where she would open herself to none but this man. She could feel herself opening now, as she never had before. . .

He raised his head. 'What was that?'

The murmur came again—nothing serious; just Al's way of asking for company.

'Let me go.' Claire drew a long, shuddering breath. 'I'd better see if there's anything he needs.'

Patrick Donovan ignored her, winged brows drawn together. 'It can't be what it sounds like.'

'It is, though.'

'A *baby*?'

'*My* baby.' She pushed herself free of him, ready to stand alone once more if she needed to. 'His name's Alexander, and he's *mine*.'

CHAPTER TWO

'MINE,' Claire said again, and at once hated herself.

What was she saying? After she'd tried so hard, all this time, to remember that Al *wasn't* hers. After she'd told herself, over and over again, that he had a real mother who must be grieving for him, and who must have him back as soon as possible.

Yet she couldn't un-say it. She knew it was her real self speaking, however little she willed it. Some hidden part of her, the same part which had tempted this man to kiss her as a woman and had returned his kiss, was now claiming Al as hers—hers by all the natural rights of love and justice.

'What the hell have you been up to?' Patrick Donovan peered into the dark corridor which led to her room.

Al, a little impatient, gurgled again. Swift as the arrow of her star sign, Sagittarius, Claire turned her back on the problem and seized her candlestick from the table, glad to lead the way towards the soothing baby noises.

'Come and meet him.'

'Just like that.' He padded after her into the dark-tiled corridor with its rows of thick, closed doors. 'I might be any neighbour dropping in.'

'I suppose you are, in a sense.' She guided him through her own doorway. 'I always leave this wide open.' She barely noted the way she made it sound as if it were a long-fixed habit—after all, that was how it felt. 'I wouldn't want him to wake up and be afraid.'

Not that he ever would. Darling Al hadn't a fearful bone in his body. Even when she'd first found him— smelly and screaming himself hoarse in his silk-draped basinette—he hadn't sounded frightened. Only angry, uncomfortable, and hungry. And once she'd changed and fed him, and cuddled him back to sleep, clean and soft and smelling of warm milk, she herself wasn't afraid any more either, except only for him.

Thank heaven she'd heard him before the power failed! She'd never ceased to be grateful for the baby-alarm which led her to him, broadcasting his amplified crying into the corridor where, on that traumatic morning two days ago, she'd been slowly, frighteningly learning that she was alone here.

The loudspeaker had stood by her door with wires trailing, as if dumped there in a hurry. It was only one oddity among many—she'd hardly noticed it until, unbelievingly, she'd heard the growing distress of a baby coming out of it. Then she'd blessed the trailing wires which led her through the labyrinth to the newer part of the building known as the Malinesi wing. Once there, she'd traced Al by sheer volume, through the portrait gallery into the airy, bright-draped room which had so clearly and expensively been fitted as a nursery.

What kind of people would surround a child with every luxury, and then leave him to starve? Or perhaps he hadn't quite been abandoned? Perhaps someone had meant her to hear and respond to those broadcast cries? She didn't know, probably never would, and, as long as Al was awake and needing her, hardly had time to wonder about it.

'Stand still until you've got your bearings,' she commanded. 'I don't want you bumping his pram.'

Dawn was glimmering across the river, she noted through the deep-set window, but they'd need their candles for a while yet. She lit the one she had set out ready on the plastered window-sill, and placed the one she was carrying on her desk.

'A *pram* for heaven's sake!' He stared in wonder at the

smart baby-carriage. 'Where are you supposed to wheel it?'

'There's miles of corridors,' she pointed out. 'And it's useful for airing him in the garden.'

'But where did it come from?'

'It was just. . .just here,' she answered, knowing no more than he did. 'Along with a lot of other stuff.'

Like bottle-sterilisers, and baby-food, and a gleaming electric kitchen for preparing it. Like a bazaar-display of bright toys, clowns and fishes and hanging stars and hall-marked silver bells. Like a baby-walker and a baby-bouncer which Al was much too young for. Like drawers full of clothes embroidered with the name Alexander, and a gold teething-ring engraved round the inside with his name followed by a mysterious, meaningful gap as if a surname might be added later.

After the gap came a date three weeks ago which must surely be that of Al's birth. It was this which had made Claire bring the teething-ring here, along with the other things that he would need, when the power went and she decided to move him here to her room. Only that, and his food, and the more practical of his clothes, and finally the little blue teddy-bear with the name Alexander tooled into its red leather collar.

The teddy-bear shared his pram, but the teething-ring was safe in her desk. It was her only clue about who he was, and her proof to herself that she meant to return him to his mother.

To distract her mind from such painful thoughts, she indicated the armchair next to the desk. 'Won't you sit down?'

She might as well not have spoken. He was staring at Al, who had kicked off his blanket again—not that it mattered in this heat—and turned to lie on his back, as he liked to do when he was awake. A gold-lit, satisfying solidness of baby curves in his blue terry sleepsuit, he blinked owlishly in the soft light and waved an apricot-pink bud of a fist at nothing in particular.

'Well, young fellow, what are we going to do with you?'

'Say hello, Al.' Claire scooped him into her arms, settled him where he fitted so comfortably against her breast, and made a place for herself to sit on her tumbled bed. 'This is your uncle. . .' She glanced up over the baby's head. 'It's Patrick, isn't it?'

'It is, but I'm not sure about the uncle.' He stayed on his feet, fearsomely tall, dark eyes fixed on Al and the new problems he raised. 'The last thing I expected on this caper was instant nephew.'

'You should be flattered; it's a title of honour.'

He made a non-committal noise. 'There are—er—other titles to be thought about——'

'Sorry to interrupt.' A glance at the baby's face had set her quickly stripping his sleepsuit. 'But now I'm having to wash his nappies by hand, this is urgent.'

In a moment she had the potty on her lap from its place in the night-table, and Al perched on it, well supported. Sure enough he needed it, and in less than a minute she was able to carry him and the potty into her bathroom for a much simplified clean-up.

'If you want to be useful, you could bring in a candle,' she called over the noise of running water.

He did, bearing it into the white-tiled vastness of the bathroom and looking for somewhere to put it. From the washbasin where she expertly cradled Al for a one-handed splash, Claire nodded at the candle already here, waiting unlit on the metal medicine-cabinet.

'Light that from it, please.'

He raised the flame he was carrying. 'How on earth did you know that was going to happen?' he asked, as the second light burned cheerfully.

'I didn't.' She sluiced the still-warm water over Al's

bottom. 'It's lucky it came in the daytime, so I was able
to collect all the candles I could find.'

'Eh? Oh.' He gestured impatiently, a black and tawny
presence in the white room. 'Not the power-cut; I meant
about him.' He nodded at the wriggling baby, who
wanted to investigate the tap.

'Being about to fill his nappy? I've always known that,
with babies.' She guided the tiny fist to the water,
enjoying the sudden, delighted stillness. 'You can tell by
the way they move, and the faces they make.'

'You mean you've *other* children?'

'Of course not.'

She laughed at the idea, and turned off the tap. Al
blinked, squared his mouth, then changed his mind and
made a grab at the towel which she was wrapping round
him.

'I'm the oldest of five,' she explained. 'I was fourteen
when little Matt was born—he's the baby. . .' She
checked herself. 'Only, he isn't any more, is he?'

'Your youngest brother?' Patrick Donovan questioned
gently.

'He's nearly ten. I haven't seen him for months.' She
held Al close in his towel. 'I meant to use up one of my
trips home, to be there on his birthday——'

She broke off, choking. A movement at her back
fluttered the candle-flames, and she felt her companion's
hand on her shoulder.

'Supposing I promise to see that you make it?'

'I don't know that I'd believe you, but. . .'

She stilled, glancing into the washbasin mirror. They
looked so right, the three of them in this gold light.
Painters down the ages had shown families thus; the
roundness of the baby doubly shielded by the softness of
the woman and the stern darkness of the man.

She turned her head to glance down at his hand,
resting so gentle and controlled and strong on her flesh.

Just as when he'd kissed her, hope sang in her blood. Hope, and something else she wouldn't, couldn't possibly think about just now. It was this other unconfessed something which made her turn at last to face him, so that his hand dropped away and Al was between them.

'But it's good to have you on my side,' she finished, and started the process of patting Al dry.

'I have to be, haven't I?' His voice was gruff. 'You're a British citizen. *Two* British citizens, for heaven's sake. . .'

'It was my mother who taught me how to look after babies.'

Claire knew she'd interrupted, knew she was babbling, but couldn't help it. In the relief at having someone to talk to it all had to come out, everything in her mind, including this chat of her beloved family and the small, everyday actions which reminded her of them.

'She taught me how to save on nappies, too.' Satisfied that Al was dry, she draped his towel one-handed over its rail. 'And aren't I glad to know it, now I can't run the washing machines.'

'You amaze me, Claire Fletcher.' But he sounded less amazed than exasperated. 'The town's going up like tinder——' he stepped back to make way for her '——and here you are blethering about nappies and washing machines.'

'If you'd ever had to do without them——' She broke off as the unkind word sank in. 'I'm sorry about the blether. It's with being alone so long,' she explained with conscious restraint.

'But surely——'

'Let's go; he might sleep again now. Don't forget the candle,' she threw over her shoulder as she led the way out.

Back in her cell, she slowed as she'd known she would, and breathed deeply. No monks had lived in Tragana

for two hundred years, but she'd often wondered if it
was their special contentment and humility which
radiated from these rough, white walls.

It certainly wasn't the shoddy, plastic-veneered furniture which calmed her like this. Her pictures must help,
though; the placid summer afternoon of Renoir's boating
party, the bright distances of Vermeer's 'Delft', and the
jewelled mosaic of the Empress Theodora which had
first drawn her to Byzantine art.

Al was another who always seemed to respond to the
peace here. He wasn't sleepy, but once she had dressed
him in his playsuit and a clean nappy he settled happily
on his front in the pram, blowing bubbles and giving the
occasional frog-kick.

Claire tidied the duvet to the back of her bed and
seated herself there, once more with a gesture to the
armchair. 'Do have this,' she urged, every inch the
dutiful hostess.

'Thanks.'

But Patrick Donovan meant 'no, thanks', refusing to
yield to the healing quiet. His tawny darkness was like a
rip in its fabric, a rip growing ever wider as he paced to
the stone-set window. Shading his eyes, he stared to
where the first light lay pearl-grey on the water.

'I take it this room faces right away from the town?'

'It's one of the reasons I love it,' she agreed, remembering the sense of space and freedom it had given her
during this last penned-up month. 'All you see from here
is river, and another country.'

'Another country.' He turned with caged-up restless-
ness to the desk. 'And you wouldn't know there was
anything going on in this one at all.'

'I didn't,' she reminded him.

'No, well, you had your own worries.' He glanced
down at Al, then pulled the office chair from her desk to
sit on its edge. 'I suppose it's lucky I dropped in.'

'So that's what you call it?'

'Not really.' The black lashes swept down and up, a little uneasily. 'It's what I meant to say to Donna, if I found her. That I just happened to be passing.' The passionate mouth parted in a reminiscing smile. 'She liked what she called the English humour.'

'What about the Leo flamboyance? Swimming here on the off-chance of finding your. . . I know, I know,' as she saw he was about to correct her again, 'of finding *any* girl, then.'

It wasn't just for her,' he pointed out, justifying himself. 'There was you.'

'Me?' In her surprise, she stopped patting Al's bottom. 'But you didn't even know me.'

'We knew you were here. A British citizen,' he explained. 'Unaccounted for, and possibly in difficulties.'

'It surely isn't part of your job to *swim* to stray Brits?'

'I might as well come clean.' He raised both hands in mock-defeat. 'It's good swimming weather. Also, the only chance ever likely to come my way to set foot in the historic Tragana Monastery.'

She nodded, understanding the lure of the forbidden island. 'This rumour that your Donna——' she caught his eye, and corrected herself '——that your. . .your *friend* was here. How long ago did you hear that?'

'Back in May. When she first disappeared.'

'So this is a state where people disappear,' she observed, not asking and not surprised. 'Weren't you frantic with worry?'

'Not really.' He spoke a little ruefully. 'That's one lady nobody'll ever have to worry about.'

'But why would they bring her to Tragana? It's not a prison.'

He shrugged. 'I don't know that they did. It's only what was being said——'

'More of a. . .barracks,' she cut in, intent on the

mystery. 'And a stately home, of course. I gather Cortesi himself stays here sometimes.'

'You'd better drop it, Claire.'

She scarcely heard. Following her Sagittarian arrow of truth wherever it should lead her, she set her tongue between her teeth and fitted her clues together one way, then another.

'Is she a friend of Cortesi? Is that why you said nobody need worry about her?'

'Drop it, I said!' He started forward, spring-coiled on the chair like a great beast of prey.

So he had his own secrets. She stared at the tightened mouth, the dark eyes suddenly hard and forbidding, and knew that he hadn't told her everything about this girl, Donna. Donna. It must be a common enough name here. One of her fellow-students at college was called that—her parents had been born here. And then there was. . .

She gasped as the clues clicked into place. 'It's Donna Cortesi, isn't it?'

'No!'

He flung his great head back, the picture of his star sign, Leo. Yet he was lying; she knew it with every truth-loving instinct of her own archer, Sagittarius.

'Right back when you first talked about her,' she persisted, defying his anger, 'you mentioned Cortesi.'

'I shouldn't take too much notice of that.' The growling undertones raged beneath the mockery. 'There's no accounting for what a man'll say at gun-point.'

His feet straddled the bright kelim rug as if it were defended territory, and his hands, equally ready for action, spanned his knees. Yet no action would work against her enquiring mind except to silence her by force, and she knew his lion's pride would never let him do that. The thought gave her the courage to press on.

'It was after you'd taken the gun away from me.' She

summoned her clear memory of every detail of their meeting. 'You said she wasn't your girl because Cortesi would never allow it.'

'I think you must have misunderstood me.' The dark eyes chilled in the light of the strengthening dawn. 'Maybe I was speaking of the way he won't allow his subjects out of the country.'

'You weren't; and anyway, he does.' Claire scrambled it out, determined not to be distracted. 'At least, when it's a promising singer and his own granddaughter.'

'Very interesting.' His voice iced over. 'How come you know so much about the family?'

'I did win the Cortesi scholarship.' Her own temper rose in the face of his hostility. 'When she sang in London this spring, they invited me to the concert, and the reception afterwards.'

She recalled the young singer vividly. Donna Cortesi had worn low-cut black velvet, with diamonds in her night-black hair and more diamonds round her moon-white throat. She had sung the splendid show-pieces of Mozart's 'Queen of the Night', her dark, starry eyes compelling the audience even though her voice clearly wasn't ready for such an exacting rôle.

'She's very beautiful. I don't wonder you——'

'How many times have I to say it?' He shot to his feet, so dauntingly tall that Al raised his head from his teddy-bear and stared. 'I had nothing whatever to do with Donna Cortesi!'

'All right, all right.' Claire laced her hands together, aware too late of her own prying impudence. 'I'm. . . I'm sorry.'

If he didn't want to talk of his own affairs, that was entirely his right. But no outburst in the world could stem the questions which she'd set moving in her own mind. She reached over to lift the teddy-bear from Al's mouth, and distracted him by waggling her finger before his eyes. Enormous eyes they were, their baby blue so dark that they would surely be black one day, like his hair. Black hair he'd have, and enormous black eyes. . .

Supposing he's Donna Cortesi's? The idea presented itself in Claire's mind in so many words. Could the aged dictator have sent his granddaughter here, to have her baby in secret?

It would explain so much. Back when she first came here, before she had understood how little movement she was allowed, she'd tried to visit the Malinesi wing to see the portraits of those eighteenth-century robber-barons who had turned the monks out of Tragana. Two guards had blocked her way, and the next day the interpreter had brought word from Colonel Danev that she must never wander there again. Supposing those orders had had to be given because Donna Cortesi was already there, and about to give birth?

It could be, Claire thought as Al made a grab for her finger. It even explains something of why they left him here.

She had puzzled over that one ever since she'd found him. Sure, you didn't take a baby where there was fighting, but how could his mother ever have gone without him?

Now Claire could see that his mother must have had no choice. Colonel Danev would make the decisions, and, in an anti-Cortesi uprising, would have to protect the family in any way he could. Maybe he'd decided the baby stood a better chance alone? Al would certainly be less clearly a Cortesi here on the island, with an English-woman looking after him.

And if that's so, she decided, more settled in her mind than she had been in two days, then I'm with them. She let Al catch her finger at last. 'Nobody's going to take it out on you, my darling, whatever anybody else has done. . .'

'And who'd do that?' the growling voice demanded.

'Eh?' She started, realising for the first time that she had addressed the baby aloud. 'Oh. Er——'

'You don't think I'd punish a baby for his mother's nosiness?'

'Of course not! What an idea. . .' She broke off, drawn against her will by the term he'd used. 'Nobody's called me Al's mother yet.'

'They must have. You could hardly have set yourself up like this——' his nod took in the pram, the teddy-bear, the pile of clean nappies on the desk '—entirely unaided.'

'Well. . .well, not in English, then,' she hedged. 'The only language I understand,' she added humbly.

'I see. So you went through your labour without a soul to speak your own language to you?'

She glanced down, shamed by the compassion in his voice. As he'd pointed out a moment ago, he was on her side even officially—it was his job to help her. But if she couldn't lie now, to him, how could she ever hope to carry off her pretence to any more hostile listener?

And pretend she must, for the sake of the baby who explored her finger so trustfully with his little toothless gums. However much her truth-loving Sagittarian instincts rebelled, she must learn to live with this falsehood and make it her friend, hers and Al's.

She drew her finger away. 'I'll have to feed him soon.'

'How soon is soon?'

'As soon as we can do without these in the kitchen.' She gestured at the candles, hardly brighter now than the eastern sky.

'Long enough.' He settled with an air of resignation on the office chair. 'It gives you time to answer a few questions.'

'Qu-questions?' She put her hand over the pulse in

her throat, sure that its hammering must be visible in the growing light.

'The details I'll need, to enter the baby on your passport.'

'Oh. Yes.' She had a nightmarish feeling of events running away with her. 'I suppose that does have to be done.'

There must be international laws against registering a baby as yours when he wasn't. And yet, hadn't Al been left in her charge, to take care of in any way that she could? And what better way to do that than to get him safe home with her, away from the conflict and beyond any suspicion of belonging to the hated ruling family?

'Did you notify your pregnancy before you left England?' Patrick Donovan asked.

'N-no.' She bit her lip, hating the swamp of deception spreading before her. 'Er—should I have done?'

'Oh, come on!' He leaned forward, more impatient than ever. 'I presume you didn't mean to start a baby like this. . .'

She shook her head ruefully. 'It's the last thing I expected.'

With good reason, she reflected, considering the quiet, bookish life she'd been leading at university. Even that unhappy affair with Trevor had finished three years ago, when she was twenty-one. Since beginning her master's degree she'd scarcely gone out with a man, let alone done what it took to get pregnant.

'But once you knew——' the deep, businesslike voice held her to the point '—you can hardly have thought the baby would just change his mind and go away?'

'S-something like that.'

He let out a small hissing noise, his opinion of such wilful blindness all too clear. 'You've at least told the father?'

She kept her gaze on Al. 'It. . .it wouldn't do any good.'

'We'll need his name.'

'I'll give it, for the documents.' She'd have time to work something out, before she had to sign anything.

'D'you think you're being fair to the guy?' he persisted. 'He'll have to help with money.' The heavy-fringed eyes, almost as dark in the growing brightness of the dawn as they had seemed by candle-light, swept from her to the baby and back. 'Maybe he'll want to do more than that.'

'I'll. . . I'll think about that side of it,' she floundered, 'when I've. . .when Al and I are safely home.'

'Ah, well, it's your own business.' He returned to his official manner. 'Language or not, you'll have noted the date of. . .'

Once more his glance dropped to the baby, and this time his eyes lit with a new warmth which was almost a smile. She could sense him accepting Al as a separate human being, whatever the people or events which had brought him into the world.

'The date of Alexander's birth,' he finished, much more softly.

She thankfully supplied the date inside the teething-ring, a rock of truth in the shifting tide of lies.

His whistle of surprise showed that he'd been adding and subtracting. 'So he's three weeks old, and you've been here a month. It's a miracle they let you board the plane.'

'I—er—I wasn't showing much.' She would have to do better than this, she realised in panic, and called on her powers of invention. 'He was a seven-month baby. Absolutely tiny. I don't know his exact weight at birth, because of the language——'

'And who was here to help you?'

'A doctor, I suppose she was,' Claire invented. 'They

brought her over from the town in a hurry, once they knew what was happening to me——'

'Can you give me her name?'

She shook her head. 'I was. . .sort of. . .busy.'

'I can see you would be.' But the dark eyes were sympathetic to her imaginary ordeal.

'And it was the middle of the night,' she rushed on, to cover her squirming sense of guilt, 'when the. . .the waters broke.'

This was better; she was beginning to get the feel of it. How lucky that she could remember that detail from her mother's pregnancies, and from the talk of family and friends.

'I. . . I had to go and wake Mara. . .' She stopped at his enquiring frown. 'You remember; that's the woman who looked after me. She must have gone with the others two days ago.'

She floundered back to the truth like a poor swimmer to dry land. 'They left all I need to look after him.' Yes, that was true, too; and so was this, as far as she knew. 'I suppose they thought we were safer here than anywhere they could take us.'

'And I suppose you are,' he agreed. 'Even if you're a bit more than I bargained for when I set off.'

He tried to speak lightly, but she couldn't fail to pick up the undertone. Every line of his body demanded action, clamoured for it with each impatient movement so that she was forced to remember his star sign. If great events were in train, a Leo needed to be at the centre of them—not here, at their quiet, forgotten edge.

'What would you have done,' she asked, 'if we hadn't been here?'

'Had a look around.' The winged brows briefly rose at what their owner clearly considered to be a silly question. 'Then gone back to the town, to see how things were developing.'

'And if——' she hesitated, gathered her courage, and spoke the name '——if Donna had been here?'

'That was only an outside chance.'

'But if she had been?'

'There's no point in talking about what might have been.'

'I think there is,' she snapped, responding to the rebuking tone. 'Seeing. . .' She grabbed her courage and raced on. 'Seeing what we were doing before Al woke up.'

'Ah.' He stood up, deliberately pinched out the three candles, and turned to survey her in the brightening day. 'Correct me if I'm wrong, but I was under the impression that that was as much your idea as mine.'

'Stop talking like an etiquette book.' Now it was her turn to rise in a fury of embarrassed indignation. 'I told you then how hard it's been for me, alone here——'

'Though not as much alone,' he glanced down at Al, 'as you led me to believe.'

'That's low, Patrick Donovan; low!' she hurled at him, hardly knowing what she was saying. 'Do you think a woman's any *less* alone because she's got a baby to look after?'

She planted herself before him and glared up into those disturbing eyes. In the full sunlight they weren't black after all, but deep, deep blue; a blue which reflected every thought as a lake reflected clouds and sunshine. Yes, sure enough, they were sober now in a way that showed her appeal had reached him.

'I'm. . . I'm sorry.' The apology was reluctant, but all the more sincere for that. 'Look, Claire, I kissed you because. . .well, because you were there.'

'Thank you.' She turned away. 'You certainly know how to turn a girl's head.'

'Which is exactly what I don't want to do,' he said

quickly, as if glad to have been given the words. 'Not now, anyway.'

'I see.' She put her hand to the pram, and knocked off its brake with her foot. 'So you don't mind kissing strange women. . .'

'Dammit, Claire, this nation's throwing off a fifty-year oppression. Aren't I entitled to be a little high about it?'

'And being high makes you randy?'

The deep blue eyes narrowed in disapproval. 'I can't say I like that way of putting it.'

'No?' She faced him again, her arm stretched behind her to keep her grip on the fluted, unyielding pram-handle. 'What would be your way?'

'Can't you see?' He seized her shoulders, forced her to stay and listen to his argument. 'The hope, the danger, the adventure, and then suddenly a beautiful girl. . .'

'Who, me?' She held to the pram-handle as to good sense, her only counter to the double assault of her blood from where those two warm hands cradled her shoulders. 'There's no need to——'

'A beautiful girl offers herself to me——'

'I did not!'

She tried to struggle free, but he wouldn't let her go. The deep blue eyes burnt into hers, burnt up her will and left her helpless to the power of that full, passionate lower lip which was coming nearer, ever nearer. . .

A disgruntled noise from Al cut through her sensual daze. She jumped back from Patrick, but he had already dropped his hands and turned from her, wiping his bare, powerful forearm across his brow.

'See what I mean?'

'That wasn't my idea!' she gasped, furious as much at her own ragged, uneven breathing as at his twisting of what had just happened—or just not happened—between them. 'It was you who——'

'Who touched you.' He raised his hands and spread

them as wide as they would go; so wide that the fingers were almost bent over backwards. 'I swear and double-swear, I won't do it again.'

And why did that make her angrier than ever? Why did she long to demand what was wrong with touching, or with their keeping each other company in this huge, oppressive loneliness? She looked down, hoping that the rose-gold of the early sun would account for the confused heat in her cheeks.

'I see I'm going to have to be wise for two. For three.' He dropped his hands and quirked his mouth humorously at a new, rather more demanding Al-noise. 'Have you quite forgotten, Claire, what you did the first time I kissed you?'

'I. . .' She forced herself to the memory of it. 'I know I kissed you back. But it was your idea,' she hurried on, justifying herself. 'It was you who pulled me up, out of the chair. . .' She stopped in obedience to his triumphant, arresting hand.

'I thought you might be making that mistake. You're speaking of the *second* time.'

'What? Of course it wasn't!'

'So you really have forgotten.' He summoned his facts with a resigned nod. 'The first time, I was merely admiring your courage. Saluting you as a comrade. It was you who—— Ah.' He broke off, satisfied. 'I see you do remember now.'

And she did. She put her hands to her hot cheeks, unable to face him, hating to be reminded of that caress which he had begun merely as a brotherly gesture, a sign of goodwill and, yes, of respect. It was she who had turned it into something else—something quite new to her experience, and not in the least respectable.

'I. . . I'm not usually like that,' she stammered. 'Not at all.'

'No, my dear,' he murmured. 'I know that.'

'Don't make fun of me.' She turned her head sharply away from the spell of those blue, essence-of-blue eyes. 'You can't possibly know that, or anything else about me.'

'I do, though. For a start——' he indicated the pram and the now slightly indignant Al '—if you'd been what you call like that, mightn't you have fixed yourself up with some birth-control?'

Oh, dear; here she was back in the tangled web. 'I could have just. . .slipped up. People do.'

'You could indeed; in fact, you did. But. . .' He paused, the tip of his tongue showing between white teeth. 'Look, I don't want to go into details, but, well, there's a lot you don't know about. . .' He hesitated again, then said what he had to. 'About men, and about making love.'

'Oh.' She rocked the pram, trying to conceal her bitter sense of hurt. 'So I don't do it very well?'

She resolutely refused to look at him, yet she knew he was scanning her from head to foot. She could feel his gaze like fire on her caught-back hair, her small head and long neck, her full breasts and narrow waist and curved hips.

'When a woman's made like you, Claire Fletcher, she doesn't need to worry about things like that.'

She whipped round to face him, convinced he was mocking her once more. But no; the fire in those blue eyes was more than just the reflection of the fiery sunrise.

'As you must have already found out,' he added, somewhat hoarse. 'Do you think I'm going to risk that——' he nodded at the pram which she still unthinkingly rocked '—happening to you again?'

'Al isn't a. . .a *that*,' she retorted, grasping at the safest of the ideas he was presenting.

'Of course he isn't.'

He moved past her, to lean over the pram and offer

both hands to the waving pink fists. Al blinked, then grabbed the strong index fingers and held on.

'Once they're here, they're people like the rest of us. You love them.' Patrick drew his fingers upwards with Al clinging to them like a monkey, and let him gently down again. 'But you've already owned he wasn't exactly what you'd planned.'

'He was certainly. . .' She kept her eyes on Al, aiming once more for that rock of truth in her swamp of lies. 'Certainly a surprise.'

'And you don't want that kind of surprise again.'

He straightened and turned towards her. She moved her gaze, but dared not raise it. Instead she kept it on the dark-tiled floor, the bright rug, his springy, high-arched feet. He'd found socks, she noted, and trainers; that was how he could still move so quietly.

'Look at me, Claire.'

And she had to do his bidding, compelled by the deep, urgent tones. The dark blue eyes held hers, clear and honest as Al's, and as open about his needs.

'Yes, I want you, and yes, that's partly because I'm. . .randy,' he admitted, accepting her slighting word. 'But I'm here to help, and that's what I'm going to do. You've been taken advantage of enough already.'

CHAPTER THREE

CLAIRE looked away, obscurely ashamed. And yet, why should she be? She was only doing the best she could for Al.

But Patrick Donovan was regarding her so honestly, with such kindness. He was so resolved to do right by her, a woman shabbily treated by some unknown man. And all the time it was she who was behaving shabbily, deceiving him with evasions and half-truths and downright lies.

'I. . . I think I'd better get this guy fed.' She turned back to the baby-carriage, and pushed it to the door. 'He'll start creating in a minute.'

Patrick joined her with a hand by hers on the pram's handle, edging her aside. 'May I?'

She resisted. 'It's not exactly heavy labour. . .'

'Please, Claire.' And, as with his earlier apology, he really meant it. 'I need to be busy.'

She stepped aside, smiling in spite of her worries. 'The king of the beasts, reduced to helping in the nursery?'

'No task is beneath me,' he told her loftily, taking full charge of Al. 'Especially if it might lead to breakfast. Have you any idea how hungry swimming makes you?'

'I'll see to it presently. But baby comes first in this family. . . I mean,' she hastily amended, 'with us.'

Which was nearly as bad. It still included this imposing near-stranger in a circle where he might not have the least interest in belonging.

Before she could try to sort it out, Al rescued her with a breathy little grunt. She had to pay attention—all Al's noises meant something. The next would be a grumble,

46

and then a warning, and, if that didn't work, then he'd really show what he could do.

'I'm glad the kitchen isn't far,' she observed as she hurried ahead along the corridor. 'He might be a Gemini, but he can roar like any lion when he wants to.'

One thing about this ancient iron stove; it did hold things indefinitely at a low heat. She'd left the pan on the coolest part, and now the sterilised feeding-bottle and its contents, lapped by body-temperature water, were exactly right.

'I do see how useful a pram is—Oh.' Settling it by the table, Patrick had glanced down to put on the brake. 'I didn't realise it was monogrammed.'

'Is it?'

She made her tone vague, playing for time as she dried the feeding-bottle. She'd been hoping that he wouldn't notice those initials on the coachwork, but she should have known better. Even here in the north-facing kitchen, now that the sun was full up, they glittered like solid gold. Maybe they *were* solid gold.

'You mean,' she parried, 'the manufacturer's logo?'

'It's not a logo. You can't have noticed it properly.'

'I haven't.'

As if she could ignore the richly crafted A within a C, scrolled with beautiful Byzantine abstracts of almost-leaves and almost-flowers. Still, she had a reasonable excuse.

'You know how it is, with a baby.'

'Have a look at it some time,' he advised, his trusting Leo soul accepting her pretence without question. 'As a student of Byzantine art, you'll be interested to find they're still doing this kind of work.'

She'd hardly have won the Cortesi scholarship without knowing that; but she had to stay silent. Must she lie even in trivial ways like this?

If only I weren't a Sagittarius, she raged inwardly at

her plain-dealing, plain-speaking birth sign. Practically anybody else could do it better.

But Al didn't have anybody else; only her. She picked him up and leaned him against her shoulder, patting his back to bring up the wind. He launched two satisfying little burps, and she was able to cradle him in her arms and offer the bottle. Ideally, she'd have preferred to do this in the armchair in her room, but you couldn't just walk out on a guest, however much you disliked his questions.

'It's an imported item, of course,' Patrick went on, still innocently inquisitive about the pram. 'They monogrammed it here for some privileged baby Cortesi, I expect.'

Oh, dear; must he? Soon he'd be seeing the resemblances she herself had seen, and asking the same questions, and all at the start of her very favourite time with Al. She sought for a way to distract him.

'Could you eat some caviare?'

'Won't it have gone off?' He glanced through one of the kitchen's small, deep windows, to where, even this early in the morning, the courtyard and high yellow wall shimmered under the midsummer sun.

She shook her head, holding Al and his bottle carefully. 'When I last looked, it was still frozen. It won't be now, though, so we should eat what we can.'

'Caviare for breakfast.' He beamed, eyes wide and nostrils dilated at the prospect of the treat. 'Lead me to it.'

'It's in the second freezer, third shelf. . . No, you'd waste the cold finding it.' She looked down in resignation at baby and bottle, linked in harmony. 'Take Al, and I'll fetch it.'

'Right, give him here.'

'He's not a parcel.' She turned protectively away to

shield the suckling baby from such a casual approach. 'Sit down, and then you can have him, if you're careful.'

He stayed on his feet. '*You're* not sitting.'

'Do you want breakfast, or don't you?'

He might almost have been about to tell her to keep her breakfast. Then his mouth lifted in that self-mocking, one-sided smile, and he sank to a plastic stacking-chair which seemed more unsuitable than ever under his neat cat-strength.

'I suppose Mother knows best.'

'Always,' she agreed seriously. 'Now keep him at this angle, and don't shake him.'

The transfer complete, she took a tray and bustled to the row of freezer-cabinets. The caviare was still nicely chilled, just enough to bring out the flavour. And here in the huge, cool pantry were the lemons, and the butter in its earthenware cooler which she had remembered to keep wet, and the long loaf of crusty local bread which was stale now, but would still toast.

'That's the biggest helping of caviare I've ever seen,' he commented on her return. 'Have they always fed you like this?'

'If you mean extravagantly, yes.' She set down her tray. 'Mara used to bring me fillet steak, and lobster, and goose-liver pâté with truffles. . .' She trailed off, reminded of all those sad, silent meals in her room. 'I used to long for a soft-boiled egg and some company.'

'Will caviare and company do?'

'It'll do very well.' Cheered by his high spirits, she opened the half-kilo pack of luscious red globules. 'How are you and Al doing?'

'Getting on fine.' He showed the round, dark head, tiny in the crook of his great arm. 'Have you noticed how his eyes close exactly with the bottle emptying? Half closed, half empty.'

'You keep them closing.' She opened the table drawer for the bread-knife. 'I'll make the toast.'

'And *you* be careful with that knife,' he countered. 'Women never cut straight.'

She drew herself up. 'Perhaps you'd like to take over?'

'I would, but I don't want to give my boy here indigestion.'

'Go on.' She watched him holding Al with exactly her own delight in his cuddly baby roundness. 'Why not admit you're enjoying feeding him?'

'It has its compensations,' he allowed grudgingly. 'What do I do now? He seems to have lost interest.'

'It's time for his midway burp.'

On hearing how it was done, Patrick insisted on doing it. He made a good job of it, and the expected gram or so of milk glopped on to the nappy which she had made him put ready on his shoulder.

'Messy boy.' He mopped Al's mouth. 'Aren't you lucky you've Mummy and me to clear up for you?'

Claire suddenly felt absurdly, exultantly pleased with life. How marvellous to be here in this diffused northern light on a sunny morning, with your son and a man who was so good with him! Held on her updraught of happiness, she cut thin, perfect slices from the loaf, and didn't in the least mind the heat from the stove when she opened it to where the wood had burnt cherry-red.

'He's finished the bottle,' Patrick called from the table, 'and his eyes are shut.'

'Good. Let's see how you are at putting him down without waking him.'

'No problem.'

And there wasn't. Al slept on, and left them to their luxurious breakfast. With some sense of living up to it, Claire wrapped the toast in a napkin and cut the lemon into squeezable pieces, filling the air with a sharpness which made her realise that she was as ready as Patrick to enjoy the subtle richness of the caviare. For a while they dedicated themselves to eating, and to the fresh coffee which she had made in the enamel percolator; and all was right with the world.

I might have known it was too good to last, Claire thought as she finished her coffee.

It was as if hunger—their own and Al's—had dulled them to the muffled noise of the gunfire. The more you ate, the more you noticed it, she decided, as a specially harsh rattle brought Patrick to his feet.

'I'll just see what's going on.' He made for the refectory, and returned a moment later with hands in pockets, discontent in every line of his slumped shoulders and idly kicking feet. 'Can't see a damn thing. I wish I knew a way of getting over there.'

She cleared dishes to the sink and instinctively kept her back turned. 'Why don't you swim, like you came?'

'Floating Al and his pram in front?' he demanded witheringly. 'Be sensible, Claire.'

She heard his indignation, but refused to look at him. 'We don't have to go with you. We'll be fine here.'

'Are you out of your mind?' He strode over and seized her shoulders, forcing her to face him. 'Do you really think I'd leave a mother and young baby here alone?'

She looked down at his hand. 'You said you weren't going to touch me again.'

'I'm. . . I'm sorry.' But his hand stayed, refusing his will, and the other stole up to match it on her other shoulder.

'Honestly, Claire; what do you take me for?'

'A lion.' She didn't try to free herself, but steadily held the blue, blue eyes. 'Trapped here by your lion's pride.'

'Maybe,' he admitted. 'I certainly couldn't live with myself if I left you two—but that's the least of it.' He kept his hands on her shoulders, his eyes fixing hers. 'I'm not going to kiss you; I'm not, I'm not. . .'

And he did, so gently and undemandingly that she just had to kiss him back, to show that it was all right. And then, of course, it wasn't all right, it was mouth on mouth, tongue on tongue, his hands leaving her shoulders and smoothing a fiery track down her spine until her body arched against him, a bow waiting for the arrow. And the arrow was ready; she could feel it. . .

'Hell!' He set her away from him and spun round to lean against the old-fashioned earthenware sink, breathing hard. 'I didn't intend putting it quite like that.'

'Supposing. . .' She cleared her throat, drew a deep breath, and started again. 'Supposing you put it in words?'

'You mean I still need to?' He turned to glance down at her in honest surprise. 'All right.' He met her steady gaze. 'I. . . I like you, Claire Fletcher.'

'And liking can mean a lot of things, Patrick Donovan. Is it just——' She broke off and looked down at the tiled floor, to stop herself glancing to where she had felt that rearing arrow.

'Certainly not.' He understood her at once. 'It's there, but it isn't just that. Not just that at all.'

'So does it mean feeling good when you're with someone?' As she'd felt at breakfast, she wanted to add; but held it in.

'Of course it does, only. . .' He trailed off and paced away from her, caged and restless as ever. 'Come on,' he called back. 'Let's take Al for a walk. You can show me the building.'

'I don't know it that well,' she admitted, but followed him willingly enough.

'This pram,' he marvelled, taking command of it. 'It's positively royal.'

Oh, dear; here they went again. 'I think they dug it out of an attic.' She crossed her fingers, and hoped that he wouldn't comment on its shiny newness. 'It. . .it was just sort of there one day.'

'You make it sound like the palace in *Beauty and the Beast*.' He unbraked the pram. 'Served by hands with no bodies.'

'It was a bit like that.' She welcomed the truth with that thankfulness which was becoming so familiar. 'Mara never talked, anyway, even if I could have understood, and I never saw any other women.'

Though there must have been at least one, in the Malinesi wing.

'Only men,' she went on, dodging that thought. 'Armed guards, every ten yards down every corridor, and several in every room; even the library. . .' She stopped abruptly, with a new idea. 'Why don't I show you that? It's this way.'

'I've been there, remember?' He directed the baby-carriage towards the distant door.

'Only in the dark, with one candle. Wait till you see the sun on that gorgeous baroque Apollo.'

'So that's who it is.' He eased the sleeping Al over the shallow step which divided kitchen from corridor. 'I can't say I care for all those billowing marble robes.'

'I didn't think I did either, but he's so. . .so cheerful.'

So full of kindly life. So civilised. So much the opposite of the stiff, impassive blue-caps and the sad, quiet Mara—the only human beings she ever saw. But she wasn't going to dwell on them, especially not now, with the sound of gunfire muffling and fading into the depth of the building.

'I got very fond of that statue,' she went on, as the tall white and gilt doors came into view at the end of the corridor. 'Maybe because I knew it before I came here. A college friend had pictures of this place.'

'Including the frescoes?'

'How did you guess?'

'You had to have learnt about them somewhere.'

'I have a degree in art history,' she told him with dignity. 'It does help you learn the odd thing or two about paintings.'

She went on ahead to open both leaves of the doors. The huge, glittering room spread before her, and she continued, from force of habit, across the pale floor to where gold-crowned Apollo played his golden lyre on his gold and marble plinth.

'So much gilt.' Patrick took in the gold-lettered plaques and gold-wreathed paintings, the gold-mounted pillars holding up a gallery decorated with gold-brimming marble urns. 'You hardly notice the books.'

'You do.' She raised both hands to the lavishness of them, shelf upon shelf of books in case after open-fronted case between each set of pillars. 'Everything's still here that the Malinesis took from the monks, and lots more. That's where I worked.' She indicated a far corner, where an office desk stood square and modest amid the magnificence. 'I've been able to read all Abbot Petar's notes on the frescoes, with English translations.'

'Supplied by Cortesi?'

'No, no. A nineteenth-century Malinesi got the texts translated into all the major European languages.'

'Trying to shake off the brigand image,' Patrick observed cynically. 'Have you seen any pictures of that family?'

'I wanted to.' She recalled her useless attempt to visit the portrait gallery. 'But the blue-caps stopped me over there, at that door.'

'Door?' He frowned in its direction. 'That's a picture.'

She laughed, and led the way to it. 'This place is full of objects made to seem like something different.'

Like the little jewel-box she'd found in the nursery, open and discarded. Its velvet padding had clearly once held a ring, but it was empty and, once closed, looked exactly like a miniature pack of playing-cards. However hard she tried, she couldn't re-open it. Who would want to disguise a ring as playing-cards, in a box you couldn't open?

'Hang on,' Patrick broke into her reverie. 'Leave that door shut a minute; I want to look.' He parked the pram, and came forward to study the painted likeness of a naked man. 'Why is he stuck all over with animals and things?'

'He's a chart really, on the effect of the Zodiac signs on parts of the body. There's you.' She showed him the lion, lordly on the chest. 'And that's me——' she pointed to where the centaur drew his bow '——in charge of the thighs.'

'The thighs, eh?' He gave her a sideways look, and hastily moved to resume control of the pram. 'Shall we go on? Though I hate to think what you have to get hold of to open that door.'

'Only this.' She pressed the door-handle, which was also the gold scythe held by the twin on the figure's right arm, and let them through into yet another corridor. 'This is where——'

She stopped, and felt the blood draining from her face. What was she doing? What had she nearly said? That it was at exactly this place, on this side of this door, that she had first heard Al's cries two days ago.

How could she have been so careless? To have dropped her guard so completely—why, they'd only need to go on a little, beyond the portrait gallery, and they'd be in that bright nursery suite with all its evidence that Al belonged to someone else.

She wheeled abruptly, blocking the pram's progress. 'Let's go back now.'

'Why?' he asked, amused. 'Will the folks at home be worrying about us?'

'I. . . I don't like those portraits,' she improvised wildly. 'They're a wicked-looking lot, the Malinesis.'

'Wicked enough to frighten the fearless Claire Fletcher? This I must see.' He manoeuvred the pram past her useless blockade, and scooped her hand into his as he passed. 'Come on. I'll take care of you.'

And how could she resist? How could she do anything but go with him, to the long, narrow room where black-eyed, black-haired Malinesis scowled from endless gilt frames.

'I know this one from the books in the library.' She pulled her hand free, and paused in relief before the exotically robed, turbanned figure. 'It's Kaspar, who built the Malinesi wing.'

'*The Necromancer*? I've seen a copy of it, too.' Patrick stared at the clever, dark eyes, the hand flourishing a pair of dividers, the celestial globe prominent on the nearby table. 'He didn't mind advertising his questionable skills, did he?'

'He could afford not to mind.' Glad to keep them here, she nodded at the jewel on Kasper's free hand. 'He had that to protect him.'

'The Devil's Eye.' Patrick stepped closer to examine the painted stone, blood-red in its rainbow-flare of diamonds. 'It's smaller than you'd expect.'

'That's because it's a true ruby,' she chattered on, her breathing a little ragged. 'They're never very big.'

'So jewels come into art history, too?'

She nodded, racking her brains for more to say. 'The books here would never call it the Devil's Eye; that's the name his enemies gave it.' She swept desperately on. 'He had lots of enemies—the monks from here, the peasants, the Turks——'

'Slow down, love.' He put a big, warm hand on her arm. 'I don't need the Malinesi story all in one breath.'

'I'm sorry.' She licked her lips. 'But. . .but it's quite interesting, don't you think?'

'It is if your bad vibes don't wake the baby.'

'My vibes aren't bad, and, anyway, it would take more than this. . .' She trailed off, unable to argue, distracted by his reference to the peacefully sleeping Al.

She was more and more sure that Al was Donna Cortesi's baby. And, however much he denied it, this man had been Donna Cortesi's lover; she was sure of that, too. And how could his ex-mistress have failed to leave some trace of herself in that far-too-near nursery suite? Something he could identify as having belonged to her? It had cupboards of expensive clothes, a dressing-table littered with scarves and stockings and lipsticks and perfume. How could he not know, when he saw them, that the woman he sought had been here?

And once he knows, she realised in despair, he's bound to start asking the same question I'm asking.

Who was Al's father? She had wondered about this ever since she had found him, and was increasingly sure that she knew the answer.

'What on earth's the matter all of a sudden?' Patrick asked, in concern. 'You're ready to burst into flames.'

'Well, I'm a Sagittarius, aren't I?' She seized the opening and galloped off with it. 'It's a fire sign, like your lion. Old Kaspar was a Leo, too, and the ruby's a Leo stone.' Ah, yes; this was what she'd been going to say. 'That one he's wearing, he called it the Tragana Flame to——'

She got no further. His hands were on her shoulders, turning her resisting body away from him.

'What are you doing?' she craned round to ask, and started forward as the movement brought her head against the broad, dark-clad chest.

'I thought so.' He pushed her forward so that his

thumbs could explore her shoulder-blades and the nape
of her neck. 'You're twanging like a guitar-string.'

'I'm not. You don't need to. . .'

She stopped as the strong thumbs soothed her back
muscles into submission. Slowly, their massage tingled
down her spine, glowed into her scalp, and sang in her
confused brain the old words her mother had been so
fond of crooning while at her chores.

'*Che sarà, sarà.* . .' her mind sang.

She heard her own voice, slow and stumbling and
languorous. 'Wh-where did you learn to do this?'

'Don't know.'

His hands paused in their slow rhythm, then slid
down her unresisting shoulders. The next moment they
were inside her jacket, lifting her breasts in the leaf-
green T-shirt.

'Maybe——' his breath came warm in her ear
'—maybe it's one of the things a guy's born knowing.'

She felt his lips on the sensitive place where her jaw
joined her neck, and drew a long, shuddering breath. He
kept his hold on her breasts, shaping them to his will
and hers. Yes, his will was hers and she would do
whatever he wanted, caught here in the fire of his arms
with the flames leaping to consume her.

'So soft,' he murmured against her cheek. 'And yet
these are like. . .like arrowheads.' His fingers played
with the exulting points. 'I want these arrows, little
archer.'

She uttered a wordless exclamation, and closed her
hands over his to push them away. But she hadn't the
strength; he held her too easily. He didn't need force,
only the skill which he had said he'd been born knowing.
She couldn't resist; had to linger with eyes shut—those
big, solid hands under hers parting and closing and
making her blood leap to their bidding.

Time stopped, until he released his hands from hers.

She let them go, aware only of a great sense of loss, and then of more and greater pleasure to come as he drew back the lapels of her jacket and lifted it away from her.

She leaned forward to slide out of it. It dropped clear and he went at once to the catch of her jeans, opening it to release the tucked-in T-shirt which he at once grasped and slid upwards, his knuckles brushing her bared abdomen.

And Al moved in his sleep.

Only that. He didn't make the least sound—not even one of his little, breathy, baby-noises—but it was enough. Claire found that her eyes were no longer unseeing; they had focused full on him, and, with the sight of him, guilt flooded her like cold water.

'Let me go.' She turned in a furious tangle of knitted cotton, and pummelled his chest with her fists. 'Aren't you ashamed, Patrick Donovan? Is this how you don't take advantage?'

For an endless moment they were frozen like that. He stared down at her, face flushed and mouth heavy but with awareness gradually returning to his half closed eyes. They closed fully, then opened, and he slowly released the cruel twists of her T-shirt.

'I'm sorry, Claire, I don't know what happened to me.' He passed a hand over his eyes. 'All I wanted, the only thing in the whole world, was to see you naked.'

'And you nearly made me want it too.'

She shuddered inwardly at the narrowness of her escape. At the very best it would have meant more lies about why she showed none of the signs of recent pregnancy. At worst, she would have found herself having to explain the inexplicable.

'Here, of all places,' she scolded to cover her fright. 'In front of horrible Kaspar and his horrible kin.'

'Do you think his Devil's Eye put a spell on me?' Patrick wiped the dark hair from his forehead and stared up at the painted ring. 'A flame, didn't you say he called it? The Tragana Flame? It just about burnt me——'

'You can't blame an old painting of somebody long dead,' she snapped. 'You've just got to grow up, Patrick Donovan.'

'What?' He seemed suddenly even taller, his chest expanding as he drew an enraged breath. 'And who are you to lecture, Miss?'

Here it came again—the part she had to play against all her instincts. 'Somebody once bitten, I suppose,' she said heavily. 'Who should know better.'

'And who's only twenty-four—yes, I know your age; we don't get that many British citizens in these parts.' He silenced her question. 'Twenty-four against my twenty-seven, *and* with a baby.'

'Women can't walk away from their mistakes the way men can,' she retorted in a fury. 'How do you know you haven't fathered a baby or two yourself, in your time——'

She broke off abruptly, the tip of her tongue caught between her teeth. Was she mad, to put such ideas into his head? Perhaps she'd be able to tell him about all this openly some day, but for now she must, must, *must* keep her one objective—to get Al out of here and safe with her to England. She stooped to rescue her jacket, flung it over the pram, and raced it away over the smooth floorboards.

His cat-like stride easily caught up. 'Where are you going?'

'I told you I didn't like it here,' she flung sideways without slowing. 'I'm going to my frescoes. *They* don't make me l-lose my head, and then fight about it.'

'Now who's blaming old paintings of people long dead?'

'I'm blaming you.'

She stuck her nose in the air, and tried to get ahead of

him with the pram. However, he had taken firm hold of it, and, before she could stop him, had raised a foot to the brake. Then he turned to her with one large palm extended.

'Come on, Claire. Don't be like that.'

She hesitated, her own hands firmly on the pram-handle.

He kept on offering his. 'There's only you and me and Al, until something happens. Friends?'

'Oh, all right.' She took it gingerly, and released it as fast as she could. 'I'm still going to my frescoes, though.'

'Can I come too? Please?' The blue eyes met hers with that sincerity which, she was beginning to learn, was his most effective weapon. 'You can tell me all about them.'

And to her surprised pleasure, she could. He asked endless questions, and she could answer them all. She was astonished to find how much her research had taught her; like how the colours had been mixed, and why the Marriage at Cana had been placed here, the Loaves and Fishes there. In the lower church, she commented on his enthusiasm.

'Why not?' he demanded. 'I'd be an idiot to waste a chance like this, to see the famous Tragana frescoes with an expert.'

'Goodness, I'm hardly——'

'Who's this?' He stood before one of the portraits, and learned that it was the Empress Irene. 'Was she really such a schemer, d'you think?'

Claire smiled. 'They've not been kind to her, have they? But look how bright the crown and necklace are, after twelve hundred years.'

'Yes, they make her look as if she liked her jewellery. That's another way she reminds me of. . .' He stopped, and turned abruptly from the painting.

'Of Donna?' Remembering that Queen of the Night in

her diamonds, Claire couldn't resist finishing the thought for him. 'She does look a bit like Donna Cortesi.'

'I told you to leave that!' He whirled to face her. 'Have you any idea what you're saying?'

'I. . . Yes, I think I do.'

And suddenly, with her eyes on the sleeping Al, she did. This child she cared for would one day want to know who he was. If she were to keep him—and she shrank from the idea of losing him—then she owed it to him to know as much as she could about the blood which was his and the union which had made him.

'It was Donna Cortesi, wasn't it?' she persisted, brave for Al as she could never have been for herself. 'That's who you had the affair with. . .'

She had to stop. With his great hand clamped over her mouth like this, the last few words hadn't made sense anyway. Helpless and furious, she watched him glance from side to side as if for eavesdroppers. Who on earth did he expect to find here among these silent, painted arches?

'Will you promise not to say another word?' he demanded through clenched teeth.

She shook her head, conveying as much of her indignation as she could with her eyes.

'Then we'll go outside.'

He marched her willy-nilly down the aisle and out of the open door. Al slept in the shade of the cloisters where they had left him, undisturbed by the fire smell or by the odd rifle-crack from the town. Patrick wheeled Claire out into the merciless sunshine, past the simple stone crosses of former monks, past the pillared Malinesi crypt, and over the hot cobblestones to the central ring of earth, where neglected roses threw their heartbreaking morning scent at the sky.

'This'll do.' He released her. 'I can't see anywhere they'd put a microphone.'

'Of all the great bullying——' She stopped as the word sank in. 'A microphone?' So that was what he'd been looking for in the church. 'You surely can't think——'

'I don't think; I know. At the embassy we have to live with the idea of them, night and day.'

'But in Tragana church!'

'*You're* visiting it regularly, aren't you?' He waved aside her disbelief so vigorously that the roses swayed their heavy heads. 'Now listen, and listen good,' he went on as their perfume eddied through the hot air. 'You are never again to talk of me and Donna Cortesi.'

'Because of her grandfather?' Claire asked, reluctantly impressed. 'Shouldn't you have thought of that sooner?'

'Maybe I should,' he agreed. 'Maybe I didn't know what I was getting into. But if any suspicion gets back to him. . .'

'He surely couldn't harm a diplomat?'

'I can always be declared *persona non grata*, but I'm not worried about that,' Patrick asserted impatiently. 'It's what he'd do to Donna. I was relieved when I heard she'd only been sent here.'

Claire wondered if deceit was starting to come naturally to her. She wasn't at all tempted to say what was in her mind; that Donna Cortesi must have been sent here to have her baby.

'Though it would be punishment enough, for her,' Patrick went on. 'She's not like you. She'd hate being hidden away here.'

'I haven't exactly enjoyed it.'

'You know what I mean. Her training broken off, her public miles away. . . Still, it could have been a lot worse.'

'She is his own family.' Claire recalled the luxury which had surrounded Al. 'I'm sure he'd never hurt her.'

'Maybe not. We don't know.' Patrick's voice came out sombre in the bright, still air. 'We don't know anything any more about that mad old man.'

He caressed a blown, dark red rose.

'If he decided she'd dishonoured the family, he might——' He broke off as if he couldn't bear to say it. 'This is a savage land, Claire. Did you know they still have the blood-feud?'

'Surely not?' Claire shuddered to think that the massacres which she'd read about in the library could still be going on. 'I read that they'd wiped it out years ago.'

'They tried. Cortesi keeps trying, but it goes too deep even for his ruthlessness.'

Patrick let the rose go, and its petals spilt on the earth like drops of blood.

CHAPTER FOUR

THE blood-feud. It spattered the history section of the library, this ferocious unwritten law that each man must avenge not only father and grandfather and brothers, but also uncles and distant cousins. Generations of men and boys had murdered and been murdered for it, and sometimes a bereaved woman had put on men's clothes, killed like a man, and died in her turn. Only powerful families like the Cortesis and the Malinesis had been able to protect themselves, and then only while their luck lasted.

And Cortesi's luck was giving out. Claire stole a glance at the pram in the shade. The blood-feud spared no males; not even babies.

I'll get you out of here, don't worry, she silently promised the sleeping Al. You're mine, and I'll look after you.

Perhaps that was the moment when she resolved to be his mother for good and all. How could she give him back, and risk his being reared on such ugliness? Supposing one day he, too, should take a weapon and set out. . .? It didn't bear thinking of.

It won't happen. I'll run any risk, tell any lie. . .

She came to herself with a start. She'd been moving her lips, making vows as she might have done in a church or law-court. She closed her mouth tight, and gave her mind to Patrick.

'So you see how it is,' he went on, unaware of the turmoil which his chance remark had started in her. 'Cortesi might have done anything to Donna, but at least he let her live.'

'I s-suppose he did,' Claire faltered.

'You mean you're not sure. Neither am I.' His restless movement scattered more petals from the roses. 'You really didn't hear or see anything——' He broke off. 'Silly question. You'd have told me long since.'

Claire kept her gaze on a late, dark red bud, still folded around its hidden heart. 'Of course I would.'

She alone must bear the burden of the lies which would free Al from the madness of this oppressed, unhappy country. He must be recognised as hers, and entered on her passport, without the slightest hint from her that it was anything but the truth.

'You'd always do anything you could to help,' Patrick added.

'I'm. . . I'm glad you think so.' Claire found that she was almost hating herself.

'Besides, you're so open.' He caressed a rose-pistil left naked on its stem. 'You couldn't hold back if you tried.'

It was exactly what she wanted him to think, so why should she feel so irritated?

'Do leave that alone.' She gestured at the long fingers still playing with the little green heart of the rose. 'How will it ever get to be a rose-hip, if you mess it about like that?'

'Eh? Oh.' He smiled, and let the future rose-hip swing away from him. 'You even want to take care of plants.'

'You think you know me so well.' She shaded her eyes to survey the trees, crosses, statues, walls, each in its shrunken pool of noonday shadow. 'But we only met a few hours ago.'

'It seems much longer.' He swatted away a wasp buzzing round the roses. 'I can't believe I ever mistook you for Donna.'

'I don't see why not.' Claire realised with surprise that it was the resemblances which she wanted him to detect, not the differences. 'We're both dark-haired, and about of an age.'

Did she hope to seem as nearly Al's mother as possible? Or were there other, deeper reasons? She veered from the question to offer another argument.

'And it was the middle of the night.'

'You're still not a bit the same.'

'I know she's better-looking than I am. . .'

'Rubbish.' The dark blue eyes swept over her tied-back hair and practical clothes. 'She makes more fuss, that's all.'

'What do you mean, fuss?' Claire remembered the exquisitely cut black velvet dress. 'I thought she turned herself out very simply.'

'Exactly. That kind of simplicity takes money, and a lot of trouble.' He frowned over the bushes to where a blackbird flirted its tail from the myrtle by the wall. 'She thought of little else. I'm still not absolutely sure whether it was me she liked, or my diplomatic privileges.'

'Duty-free imports, you mean?'

'You'd never know it here——' he nodded at the massive building beyond the cloisters '——but life's hard in this country. She wanted make-up, fashions, jewellery—you know the kind of thing.'

Claire did. 'Couldn't she bring them back from her travels?'

'She did, and imported them on her own account. Nothing was ever enough.'

'So you got more for her?'

'Gifts for all occasions, that was me,' he admitted ruefully. 'Not that those were ever enough, either.'

'Was she really so. . .so greedy?' Claire hesitated over the word, hating to use it of the woman who was probably Al's mother.

'I dare say I encouraged it.' The one-sided, self-mocking smile flashed briefly. 'Leos like giving presents, don't they?'

'And hate being taken for granted,' Claire confirmed. 'Maybe she just stopped asking nicely?'

'Asking—er—nicely,' he took up the phrase with an air of restraint, 'wasn't her style. She didn't ask, she ordered.'

'A strong-minded lady, then.'

Claire recalled Donna Cortesi's concert. The platform had been banked with flowering shrubs, waxy, perfect camellias and magnolias, and drifts of fragile wistaria. The singer herself had initially seemed fragile against the dark sheen of the grand piano; but not for long. She governed her pianist with tiny, implacable gestures, and quickly took her audience into the palm of one expressive, red-tipped hand.

'She certainly has star quality,' Claire added with a sigh.

'I'll tell you something about stars.' Patrick spoke softly, almost hesitantly. 'They may glitter, but they're cold.'

'Cold!'

'Is that so surprising?'

'Yes. . .no. . . I mean, well. . .'

Here they went again into the quicksands of deceit. How did you explain that *coldness* was the last thing you'd expect of a woman so carried away by passion that she'd let herself fall pregnant? Yes, and brought the baby to full term, and given it the same luxuries which she enjoyed herself?

'She. . .she just didn't seem like that when I saw her,' Claire explained feebly.

'No, well, you were her public, weren't you? I was one of those myself, once.' He turned restlessly. 'But how would you ever understand the likes of her? You're so much. . .softer.'

'Softer!' Claire repeated with wrath. 'If you knew

what it's been like here for the last month, let alone the last two days. . .'

'I didn't mean weaker—would I ever say that about you? What you are,' he sought for another way of putting it, 'is tender. Open. Good——'

'You make me sound like. . .like a soft-boiled egg!' she broke in. 'Utterly boring.'

'I've always enjoyed a nice soft-boiled egg.' He smiled at the silly image, and suddenly the blue eyes were full on her. 'But did I say boring? Did I?'

'Tender, open, th-those are. . .' she tried, but couldn't meet the burning, dark blue gaze '. . .dead-boring things to be.'

'No, they're not. But an egg in any form you also are not.' The one-sided smile this time included her in its mockery. 'If we're going domestic, try a garden.' He thought for a moment. 'No, a meadow. That's you; a meadow ready for cutting.'

'Cutting?' She put an embarrassed hand to her hair.

'Lush, and as sweet as high summer.' He took possession of the hand. 'And with a walk like grass in the wind.'

She moved her lips, but no words would come. She was too conscious of the lean height of him, the dark blue eyes blazing into hers, and the strong hand grasping her own. Already a pulsing weakness was spreading from that warm, unyielding grip. If she didn't move soon she'd be lost, and yet the stirring of her feet only brought her closer to him.

'Watching you walk, a man could forget his hopes of heaven,' he murmured, so close that his breath fanned her cheek. 'And then you talk to your baby with a voice like milk. . .'

'There you go again.'

But she couldn't move; not her cheek from the nearness of his lips, not her wrist from his grip. Something in her leaped and rejoiced, and not only at his taking for granted that Al was hers. She sought for words to rescue herself.

'You could hardly get more everyday than milk.'

'There's nothing everyday about you, Claire Fletcher——' He broke off. 'How strange. Your name means arrow-maker.'

She nodded, glad of the distraction. 'Perhaps that's why I'm so zodiac-minded.'

'Didn't you say Sagittarius was a fire sign?'

'L-like Leo.'

'I knew it. There's fire in you, little arrow-maker.' The words blew softly on her cheek. 'I can see it in your eyes.'

'N-no you can't,' she contradicted desperately. 'Th-they're grey. Grey as rain.'

'Rain be damned; they're grey like today's first light, with the sun promised. Let me see them.'

'No.'

If she couldn't escape, she could at least lower her lashes and turn her head away. But when he cupped her chin in one hand, she couldn't resist; she had to let him raise her face to his gaze.

'If you don't let me see your eyes,' he threatened, 'I'll kiss them.'

That did it.

'You dare!' At last she could try to break free, and when she failed she glared up at him.

'Got them!' he exclaimed in triumph. 'And I was wrong about first light. They're a darker grey than that.'

'And yours are as blue as blarney,' she snapped. 'You're not called Donovan for nothing, are you?'

'I still want to kiss them.' He stared down at her, unrepentant. 'And not only your eyes, little arrow-maker.'

'Then want must be your master.' She prised uselessly

with her left hand at the strong fingers enclosing her right. '*Will* you let me go? It's time for Al's next feed.'

'Can I give it to him?'

'Only if you're good.'

'I'm good.'

He opened his hand and she was free. Yet as she escaped him she was conscious of a shadowy chill in the hot noonday light. Only when she reached the cloisters and the newly waking Al did she recognise it as loneliness.

It stayed with her until Patrick sauntered to her side, and took up his self-appointed task with the pram. Then there were other things to think of: collecting the nappies which she'd draped to dry on the lavender and rosemary bushes in the kitchen garden, and breaking a sprig of the rosemary and a leaf of bay, and asking him to harvest a lettuce and some potatoes.

'You'll find a gardening-fork in there.' She spoke above a new noise, a distant droning, as she indicated the cool, half-underground chamber which served as a storeroom. 'And some wood while you're about it, please, for the stove. . . What is it?'

The question was both drowned and answered as the helicopter roared shatteringly overhead. Claire rushed to pick up and comfort the frightened baby, Patrick raised both arms to signal a double-victory sign, and the flashy blue-and-silver object passed on.

'That's Cortesi's personal transport.' Patrick's eyes shot blue sparks of excitement in the brilliant noonday light. 'Hell and damnation, I wish I knew what's happening!'

'But until we do, we might as well eat.' Claire felt very stodgy and grown-up, soothing Al against her shoulder and bringing them all back to life's basic needs. 'The wood, please.'

She had already decided which of the perishable

wealth of food at her disposal she would cook next. By the time she had Al changed, Patrick had finished his tasks, but she wouldn't let him top up the fire.

'Wait till we've eaten. Take this——' she handed him a fire-iron '—and open the stove.'

While she cuddled the fresh-nappied, lavender-scented baby, he hooked up the heavy iron lid as she directed. He inspected the arrangement of iron bars over the grey-red heart of the fire, and she showed him the charcoal she had found, and the prime beef steaks she had set to marinade before breakfast.

'A barbecue!' he exclaimed in delight. 'You're amazing, Claire Fletcher.'

'Never mind about that.' She nodded at the chair which she had begun to think of as his. 'You take care of our boy here.'

Patrick seated himself without argument, and Claire handed over the baby. Al's brief grizzling had long been replaced by an expression of placid enquiry. He blinked as he felt Patrick's arms supporting him, blew a bubble, and without the slightest warning favoured the world with one of the landmarks of babyhood.

'He's smiling,' she burst out in delight at the engaging, gummy grin. 'A real smile, not just wind.'

Patrick lifted the bottle high in celebration, then offered it to his willing charge. 'This child,' he observed when Al at once got down to business, 'knows what's good for him.'

'Wise child,' she agreed, and suppressed a guilty pang as the rest of the saying echoed in her mind.

Maybe Al *did* know his own father. May he was responding to some mystic bond, some call of gene to gene which flowed deeper and stronger than anything she could offer. Maybe that was what had brought on so early this marvellous moment of the first smile. The idea helped her conquer any resentment she might feel that it hadn't been for her.

After all, it was good to know that Al had a father—if this *was* his father—who could manage him so well. When the bottle was empty, Patrick rocked him to sleep and settled him in his pram before mooching over to where she was busy with her cooking tasks.

'I suppose I couldn't take over that now?'

Claire patted the lettuce dry, and nodded at the new potatoes waiting in the bowl. 'You could scrape those.'

'Oh.' He picked up the long fork to wave at the steaks, still marinading with the bay and rosemary which she had added. 'I really meant, could I do these?'

'It's too soon.' She took the fork from him and put it down. 'Anyway, I don't see why you should have all the fun jobs.'

'Supposing I offer to do the washing-up as well?'

'And Al's bottles? They'll need sterilising.'

'If you'll show me how.'

'And you'll get the potatoes cooking before you start? And not toss the salad——' she nodded at the oil-and-vinegar dressing which she had mixed '—till the rest's nearly done?'

'Please,' he rebuked with dignity. 'If there's one thing I've learnt in my long life, it's how to time steak and salad.'

'And you'll really do the dishes?' She recalled her brothers' easygoing attitudes to the task. 'Straight away?'

'Cross my heart.' The dark blue eyes met hers in transparent honesty as he sketched a cross over the left side of his broad chest, then drew a finger across his throat. 'And hope to die.'

'It's all yours, then.' She untied her huge, white apron. 'I'm off to wash nappies.'

The bathroom hot water was no more than lukewarm

now, but Claire reckoned that it was the rinsing which
mattered. She rinsed and rinsed, wrung and wrung, and
at last splashed her own face in agreeably cold water.
Patrick came to the open door of her room while she was
rubbing cream into her hands.

'How does *madame* prefer her steak?' he asked
ceremoniously.

'Medium.' She joined the game with an air of mock-
disdain. 'And tell the chef to make sure the plates are
hot.'

'As if I'd ever——' He broke off, and resumed his
stately pose. 'I shall serve *madame* in ten minutes.'

'Do so.'

Perhaps it was his mock-formality which sent her to
find her favourite sleeveless grey-blue dress. It might
only be cotton, but its fineness swirled like smoke with
the occasional nasturtium flame. She adjusted its draw-
string neckline to midway, and the air cooled her
shoulders agreeably, then she loosened her hair and let
it cascade to her waist. Now it only remained to darken
her eyelids to blue-grey, brighten her mouth to nasturtium, and thrust her feet into her favourite tiny gilded
sandals.

'I'll give him meadows ready for cutting!' She brushed
her hair to a black-molasses sheen, and drifted into the
kitchen with minutes to spare.

'Delicious.' Patrick was tossing salad with his back to
her, and had just stolen a crisp heart-leaf to taste. 'What
did you put in. . . My God!' He jumped to attention, his
casual glance snapped to an unashamed stare. 'All that
in ten minutes?'

'It's. . .it's cooler,' she stammered.

'Oh, certainly.'

Was that irony in his tone as he eyed the curtains of
hair round her neck and shoulders? She pushed it from
one hot cheek.

'If I keep it tied up for too long it gives me a headache.'

It was true; but only as she said it was she aware that she did have a headache. It pounded at her temples while she took her seat at the table, and her eyes felt gritty and dry with over-use.

Looking at Patrick, she saw reflected in him what must be her own state of fatigue. His features were drawn and hollow, the strong nose more prominent, the shadows under the eyes almost as dark as the eyes themselves.

'How long is it since you slept?' she asked, as he put the salad by her.

'Hm? Oh. Well, now.' He made for the stove, and returned with a shell-thin, cobalt and gilt plate. 'Last night I was driving, swimming, and meeting beautiful girls and babies.'

He set the plate before her. She surveyed it critically, but couldn't fault the tiny new potatoes, or the brown, juicy steak appetisingly barred with grill-lines. Tantalised by the aroma of charcoal and good meat, she could hardly wait to begin, and quickly piled salad on her cobalt and gilt side-plate.

'The night before,' he went on, 'I had to be at a party until the small hours.'

'Do you go to many parties like that?'

'All the time.' He set a sauce-boat beside her. 'Your marinade smelt so good, I heated it for gravy.'

'It's the fresh herbs, I expect.' She used the gravy-spoon to push aside the bay-leaf, and took a little of the sharp, fragrant mixture. 'So you're much in demand, then?'

'Eh?' He brought over his own plate and seated himself cornerwise to her. 'Because I go to lots of parties? Have you enough of this for now?' He waited for her nod, and took the salad bowl in his turn. 'You should see the parties.'

'I can imagine them.'

And she could. They'd be in splendid rooms, with waiters in white jackets and elegant, bejewelled women who must surely flock to him—he'd be superb in evening clothes. And one of those women of course, would have been the glamorous Donna Cortesi.

'No wonder I. . .step out of line,' he added, tackling his plateful. 'You never saw such a crowd.'

'So beautiful?' she asked wistfully.

'What?' He put his knife and fork down to stare, then took them up in resignation. 'Oh, well. I suppose you can't expect outsiders to understand.'

'No,' she agreed, chilled by this distanced view of herself. 'Not us outsiders.'

'Now don't get huffy, Claire, it's not like you.'

'You're doing it again.' She cut a piece of her butter-soft steak. 'We met less than twelve hours ago. How on earth do you know what I'm——'

She had to stop there. The meat tasted even better than it smelled and looked and cut; so good that it would have been a shame to argue through it. And then, the more she ate of it, the more harmonious she felt. Patrick finished the salad and the spare potatoes which he'd left keeping hot, and then brought out the plain, rich chocolate-cake he'd found in the pantry.

Claire refused that, and carried dishes to the sink while he ate his share. By then she felt so content that she could almost have washed them with hot water from her permanent stove-kettle, but she remembered his promise, and did no more than pile them to soak.

'That was really something.' He stretched mightily, legs vanishing in the shadows under the table, arms endlessly outspread, tousled dark head thrown back on the strong neck. 'If I'd no other reason to remember you, Claire Fletcher, I'd never forget our food.' He turned his head to follow her movements as she took away his cake plate. 'What shall we do now?'

She continued to the sink, and waited for him to remember his promise. He didn't; but then, he was very tired. Perhaps the dishes could wait, after all.

'I think you should rest.' She had the oddest feeling of talking to a slightly older Al. 'There are other beds in rooms near mine, on the lay-brothers' corridor. I'll show you.'

'You can show me,' he conceded. 'But I doubt I'll sleep.'

'We'll see.'

'I haven't seen a quarter of this place yet.' He smothered a yawn. 'And I'll never get another chance.'

Alarm bells rang in Claire's mind. If he went exploring, it would only be a matter of time before he discovered that luxurious nursery and all the feminine trappings which must surely have belonged to Donna Cortesi. That Liberty silk scarf, for instance, and the cameo brooch set in hallmarked Victorian silver. Might they not be things which he himself had given her?

Don't panic, she scolded herself. He's dead on his feet. I bet if he sees a bed, he'll fall into it.

He certainly was sleepy. When she took charge of the pram, he didn't protest, only followed her along the corridor to the door next to hers. She opened it to show the mirror-image of her own room, its bathroom giving off the opposite way.

'I'll get sheets.'

'Don't.' He walked past her and sat down, swaying forward on the cheap blue nylon bedspread. 'I won't be needing them.'

His eyes were shut, she noted, as she stepped inside the door and closed it. 'I agree, you'd sleep without them.'

'No, I wouldn't!' He started up and loped across to

rejoin her. 'I told you, I'm not sleeping. Quite apart from the waste, what if something happens?'

'I'd wake you.' She held her ground against the closed door. 'Go and lie down,' she ordered. 'If you do that, and stay awake long enough to tell me you're not sleepy, I might believe you.'

'Bossy-boots.'

'Mule-head.'

For a moment longer they faced each other. He towered over her, his back to the drowsy-afternoon light, his face in shadow so that she couldn't tell whether he meant to be sensible or to argue further—even perhaps to put her physically out of his way.

She tossed back her hair and summoned all her strength. If she couldn't prevent him leaving here and sightseeing through the monastery, then she must go with him, and do all she could to keep him from the nursery quarters in the Malinesi wing. But the first answer was to hold him here, any way she could. . .

'Right.' He swooped forward, and swung her up into his arms.

Any way but this!

'Stop!' she squeaked as the room whirled and her hair dragged between her back and his arm. 'What are you doing?'

'Going to bed like a good boy.' He set her on the slippery, nylon bedspread. 'Nanny doesn't mind if I bring along something soft to cuddle, does she?'

'L-let me go at once! How dare you. . .?'

And then she couldn't speak or even think any more, only feel. All that mattered was his hungry mouth on hers, the answering hunger which sent her tongue to his. Her hands stole to the rounded biceps and wide shoulders, and then the broad chest and narrow hips pressed her into the mattress, and the sinewy thighs flaunted their proud message through several layers of clothing.

'No!' She pushed him away in terror, trying to struggle up to a sitting position. 'Please stop.'

His only answer was to pull at the draw-string neck-line of her dress. 'I love undoing parcels.'

'But I'm not a parcel, I'm *me*. . .'

Her protecting hands were useless, her anguished movements only shrugged the dress down to her waist. Now he'd somehow loosened her back-fastening bra and flung it away, leaving her abundant breasts open for his enjoyment.

And hers! She gasped, closed her eyes, huddled herself together, but that only made it easier for his mischievous tongue to skip from one crest to another and back, taking each in turn into his mouth, circling and whetting and sharpening until her whole body seemed dissolved in flame.

'Such softness.' He pushed them together, and stirred them anew with his cheek. 'Such hardness. That's you, little archer, soft and hard together.'

'No!'

She almost whimpered it, trying and failing to stop him undoing her belt. It fell away, and the folds of cotton slid from her small waist, showing ever more of her smooth, flat, unmarked belly. He hadn't noticed it yet—he was playing with her hair—but when he did. . .

Who was that, weeping like a lost child? The sobs went on and on, racking her body so that he raised his head from the swathes of her hair to stare at her.

'I only want to love you, my darling,' he murmured, husky with desire. 'Is that so bad?'

'You d-don't,' she sobbed. 'That's not love, it's hateful, selfish pleasuring.'

'Selfish!'

She could almost see the word taking hold. The blue-sparking eyes darkened to a thoughtfulness which drew together the eagle's-wing brows. The long mouth thinned as he understood what he was doing and took control of himself. Slowly, deliberately, he sat up and swung his feet to the floor.

'I suppose this is how Al happened in the first place?'

She seized the subject with relief. 'I already have one child to take care of, and you didn't care if I got another.'

'So you're not fitted up. . .' He turned away from her, head bowed. 'I suppose you wouldn't be. Birth control's illegal in this country.'

'And yet you never thought about it.' She dashed her tears with the back of her hand. 'Not for a minute.'

'I'm——' He broke off, stood up and prowled a few steps, then turned to face her across the distance which he had put between them. 'I'm a hot-blooded guy.'

'And what would you have done,' she demanded, pressing her advantage, 'if your hot blood had got me another baby?'

'Why, I'd——' He stopped, and stared at her. 'I'd have married you.'

'What?' She crushed down her wretched, treacherous pleasure, telling herself in exasperation how typical it was of him to mention it so lightly. 'And when do I get *my* say?'

'You've given it.' His gaze dropped to her breasts, each with its flaring signal. 'You've been giving it ever since I first kissed you last night.'

'I have not!' She glanced down at herself, and in one appalled movement wriggled her feet to the floor so that she could pull her dress up to decency. 'Do *you* want to marry every girl you're attracted to?'

'No, but——'

'Then why do you think I'd want to marry *you*, just because I'm. . .' She faltered as she saw his expression harden.

'I see what you mean.' His voice had taken on a grating note. 'After all, you've managed without it once, haven't you?'

'Oh, you. . .' She bit her lip, forcing back the renewed gush of tears. 'Would you mind turning your back, please, while I see what damage you've done to my dress?'

He strode to the window to stare out at the fast-flowing river and the next-door country, which was blue with heat-haze. 'I've never so much as mentioned marriage to any girl before.'

'I'll bet.' She picked up her bra from where he'd dropped it, and started untangling it. 'Marriage, responsibility, you don't know what any of it means.'

'Yes, I do.' He fidgeted and stamped at the window. 'I'd take on you, and Al, and any child we might. . . I'd take you all on, if I had to.'

'Thank you. That certainly is a tempting offer.'

'You're not giving me time to think.'

'What time were you giving *me* to think?' The damned shoulder-strap wouldn't shake out straight. 'I keep telling you that we hardly know each other, yet I'm supposed to risk——'

'All right, all right! You've made your point.'

'I haven't even begun to make it.' At last she could lean her breasts into the cups of the bra. 'You've never thought about things like this in all your life, have you, Patrick Donovan?'

He whirled about to retort, but instead only swallowed hard. She went on leaning forward, fumbling at the back-fastening, clumsy with her awareness of his gaze.

'I suppose I couldn't just kiss them? Once each?'

'Don't you ever give up?' She got the thing fastened, and dragged her dress into place over it. 'You're like a boy in a sweet-shop.'

'An orchard,' he corrected her wistfully. 'Your body's all ripe fruit. . .'

'There you go again.' She pulled the draw-string neckline as high as it would go, right up to her throat, and thankfully tied it. 'I'm no more an orchard than I am a parcel, and if you weren't such a greedy school-boy——'

'That's enough,' he cut in, eyes like blue lightning. 'If you didn't want me, why the hell did you change into that dress?'

'I told you.' She looked down to the belt she was fastening, biting her lip. 'To be cool.'

'Oh, yes? And the hair?'

'To. . .to ease my headache.' It sounded lame, and yet when she put her hand to her eyes the throb was still there, pounding the red-shot darkness behind them. 'What is this, anyway?' she demanded. 'Must I choose my clothes to fend off possible rape?'

'It wouldn't have been rape.'

He wasn't arguing now; he was too sure for that. So sure that she could have kicked him.

'Yes, it would,' she asserted wildly. 'I brought you here to rest, not to maul me about. . .'

'To *what*?' He breathed hard, his Leo pride outraged. 'I have never in my life *mauled* a woman *about*.'

'I'd rather hear from the women on that.' She shot to the door, and flounced round. 'All those parcels and orchards and chocolates might turn out to have something different to say.'

'And I'd like to hear from Al's father.' He sprang across the room, too angry to stand still, and flung himself down to sit on the edge of the bed. 'I wonder how he managed to keep you quiet long enough to get you pregnant.'

'How did *you* manage it?' she demanded, hardly

knowing what she was saying. 'I'll tell you how—by not bothering. As long as you enjoyed the sex——'

'What the hell would you know about enjoying sex?' He sat bolt upright, fists gathering great swaths of the unfortunate blue nylon bedspread. 'All you do is order me about.'

She took a deep, tremulous breath. He would never know how grateful she was for his interruption. But for that, heaven knew what she might have told him.

And she didn't need that. She could show him his character without the least difficulty, just from the small everyday details of the time they'd spent together.

'I'd sooner bring up any number of babies alone than marry you, Patrick Donovan.' It came out breathless but quiet, and she was able to fix him with her eyes as she spoke. 'It would be a lot less trouble in the long run.'

'Why, you little——' He stopped, swallowed, and mastered his temper. 'It's manners to wait till you're asked.'

'You were the one. . .' She controlled herself. 'When you do ask, make sure the unlucky lady hasn't seen you the way I have during these past few hours.'

'What?' Clearly, he couldn't believe his ears. 'After I've fed your baby. . .'

'Leaving me to change him, and wash the nappies.'

'But dammit, he's *your* baby, isn't he?'

'And feeding him and cuddling him are the nice parts. You got those, I did the chores.'

'Well, then——' he changed ground '—didn't I cook for you?'

'After I'd done all the planning and preparing. And,' she threw at him in triumph, the grievance out at last, 'the washing-up's still waiting in the sink. You haven't even thought about it; that's what your promises are worth.'

'I'll do it now.' He jumped up, gaunt with fatigue. 'Out of my way.'

'So, you see, I'm not surprised to find that you want your sex the same way,' she rushed on, determined to finish. 'All the fun, none of the chores.'

She turned, opened the door, and dodged out of it in front of him. In the corridor, however, she gasped, and only stopped herself from screaming by putting both hands over her mouth.

A thin-faced, worried-looking army officer had Al in his arms, and was pointing a pistol straight at her.

CHAPTER FIVE

CLAIRE's first act was to grab her baby. Her single-minded lunge took the man completely by surprise, and the gun clattered to the floor just as Patrick followed her to the door to complicate things in his dark Forget-me-not T-shirt and trousers.

Al's grizzling swelled to outrage at her roughness, but she had no time to worry about that. She must get her bare foot to that gun, and kick it as far out of reach as it would go. It was a good kick, her toes ached from it, but she only noticed later how the foul thing had skidded over the dark, marble tiles and come to rest at the wall. At the time she was too deafened by Al, and too busy confronting the officer who might attack Patrick as a Forget-me-not.

'He's English.' She jerked her head to show who she meant, and tried the local version of the word. '*Anglichse!*'

'Is OK.' The man had to shout to be heard over Al. 'Is gun only against *myosoti*, Mees Fletchair.'

'You. . .you know me?' Claire held Al against her shoulder, patted his back, and shouted as quietly as possible so as not to upset him further. 'How. . .'

The officer either couldn't hear, or was more interested in greeting Patrick. He had stepped round her, hand outstretched.

'Meester Dunofan! We find your car, your clothes. We think maybe you drown.'

'Kapitan Todoresi!' Patrick still breathed hard, but his eyes no longer flashed blue lightning, and his deep tones, easily cutting through Al's, rose in welcome. 'What brings you here?'

85

'Helicoptair, boat,' the officer bellowed with literal simplicity as he bent for his gun and stuck it back in its holster. 'Boat wait now; we search for Cortesi.'

'I'm sure he's not here.' Claire had noted Al's wet nappy, and knew she should change it, but couldn't drag herself away so soon from this news of the outside world. 'What's going on? How do you two know each other?'

'The *kapitan* is. . .was, I suppose I should say,' Patrick corrected himself, ever smoother as his breathing quietened, 'in charge of the soldiers who patrol the embassies.'

'They make you have soldiers in the embassy? I thought it was technically——'

'Outside it, idiot.' He didn't crack a hint of a smile at her mistake, or of understanding for her confusion. 'The *kapitan* and I also liaised on permits and such.' He returned eagerly to the new arrival. 'What's happened back there, then?'

'The *myosoti*. . .' The *kapitan* stopped, and gestured at Al. 'Is you who make it cry so, Mees Fletchair, not I.'

Patrick stepped forward. 'Give him here.'

Before Claire could protest, he had taken the roaring baby. For a marvellous moment Al quietened with sheer surprise, then started again louder than ever. Claire watched with perverse satisfaction as Patrick rocked him, crooned nonsense in that deep voice, called him a cry-baby, promised him a fire-engine, an express-train, a moon-rocket.

'Try a dry nappy,' she bawled sourly.

He cast her a glance of pure hatred which showed that he hadn't forgotten a single word of her taunts. 'I will.'

He turned, and made for her room with the baby. Only her hunger for news held her from starting after him—that, and some instinct of courtesy to the new arrival. Also, she realised more slowly, it was sheer bliss not to have that screeching right next to her ear any more.

'Don't forget to wash and dry him thoroughly,' she shouted. 'And it's wise to. . .'

She might as well have saved her breath; he'd banged the door. Al's clamour still rang through the thick, ancient oak, but her own voice would never penetrate it.

'He cry little, in baby-wagon.' The *kapitan* gestured to the pram in the blessed quiet. 'That is why I pick up.'

'He was wet,' she explained shortly.

Crying little, as he'd put it, was Al's only signal—how could she have ignored it? Worse than ignored; closed the thick door so that she couldn't even hear it. That was Patrick's fault; first his stubbornness and then his greed and then his temper.

'I love children, Mees Fletchair. You have not baby when you come here?'

'He's only three weeks old.' Claire crossed her fingers behind her back, and hastily changed the subject. 'How do you know about my coming here, *kapitan*?'

'I arrange escort from airport,' the little man told her with some pride. 'To gate of Kalavesi Palace. After that——' his face darkened '—*myosoti* take you to President Cortesi.'

'*Myosoti*.' Claire remembered the gilded wrought-iron gates of the Kalavesi Palace, the endless avenue of savagely pollarded lime trees, the blue-uniformed guards with their bright blue caps standing all the way along it at twelve-foot intervals. 'Is that your word for the Forget-me-nots?'

'Is little blue flower, yes? And now they hide, they shoot. When we find Cortesi,' the little man went on soberly, 'maybe they stop.' He nodded to a couple of soldiers, subdued and summer-clad like himself in short-sleeved drill tunics, who had appeared at the cloister end of the corridor. 'They not like search here,' he explained as they gingerly opened doors and disappeared into each room in turn. 'Is holy.'

'It's quite empty, but for us. I've been all over it——'

Claire broke off with a hunted glance down the corridor. Had they found the nursery? If they had, what were they thinking? If they hadn't, what would happen when they did? She listened with half an ear while the *kapitan* explained how every possible corner must be checked, however unlikely.

From her room, Al had already quietened. Patrick must be doing something right—unlike what he'd been doing ten minutes ago. She felt a blush spreading right down her neck and shoulders, and tried to disguise it by putting a hand to her tangled hair.

'Er—will you excuse me while I tidy up?'

Not waiting for an answer, she dodged into the room where Patrick had so mistreated her. She didn't dare close the door; they might think she was hiding something worse. She just had to tolerate the man's knowing stare as she shook out and flattened the bedspread, ran to the wall-mirror and smoothed her hair as well as she could without a comb, evened up her neckline, pulled at the belted-in folds of her dress, and thrust her feet into the gold sandals which she must have lost at some time during Patrick's grab.

To have done this to me, and risked worse, she fumed to her reflection, hating Patrick more than ever. Even as it is, with Al and all, these men must be thinking I'm a. . .a. . .

But she couldn't bear to use any of the words that came into her mind to describe what Patrick had made her seem. He was nothing but a crude, greedy, over-sexed, infantile. . .

'What is it?' She jumped at the hesitant knock.

The *kapitan* had gone, leaving at the door a round-faced, military-service-at-eighteen conscript. She returned the boy's smitten, embarrassed grin with a brief nod—here was another man who had grounds for thinking that she was no better than she should be—and made way for him to get on with his search.

Once in the corridor, she followed the male rumbles to her own room. The *kapitan* was perched on her desk, earnestly explaining something in his own language. Patrick sat on the bed, dancing the blue teddy-bear for Al, whom he held easily in the crook of an arm while listening with grave attention. Al—the little fink—glowed with enjoyment.

'All boys together, I see,' she observed from the doorway.

Patrick ignored her, asking an incomprehensible question. Only when he had the answer did he turn to her.

'Get packing.'

'What?' She didn't move, taken aback by the cold command.

'Plane go tonight,' the *kapitan* explained. 'Not wait.'

'What plane? Where am I supposed to——'

'The British Embassy's right in the firing-line.' Patrick stood up, dropping the teddy-bear. 'Women and children leave tonight, and you——' he glanced down at Al '—are going with them.'

'But. . .but. . .'

Patrick put Al into the waiting pram, and turned back to Claire. 'Get what you can into one small suitcase. I'll feed Al, and do what I can to help.'

'But how do you know I want to go?'

'You're going.'

'My baby,' she foundered incoherently. 'My passport. . .'

'It's all right.' The midnight-blue ice of his eyes melted a little. 'I'll be in touch with the London office about that. Don't worry, we'll sort it out.'

And then she scarcely had time to think, let alone argue. Patrick objected to her having a shower, but finally agreed it would be all right if she was quick.

'Strictly no shampoo, no lotions, no fal-lals,' he warned, as he and the *kapitan* departed with Al. 'You're going when the boat does, ready or no.'

The shower at least was refreshing, and slightly eased her headache. She scarcely bothered to dry herself, but found a fresh T-shirt, and seized with relief on the trousers and blouson which she had been wearing when Patrick first arrived. What a fool she'd been ever to change out of it!

Then it was only a matter of catching her hair once more to the crown of her head. The headache throbbed up again, but she wouldn't let it slow her. She fetched the smallest of her cases from the wardrobe, and threw her notes into it, and her sketches and photographs of the frescoes. Then she piled in bibs, muslin nappies, plastic pants, zinc ointment, all of Al's endless needs for a journey which was bound to be a nightmare.

'All right, you can come back in,' she called to the firm double knock.

Presumably the *kapitan* was about his duties. Only Patrick appeared, with Al in his pram.

'Am I being discreet enough for you?'

'You're a bit late thinking of that.' She told herself that the flood of heat to her face was caused by pure anger, and flapped open Al's hand-crocheted shawl. 'We won't be able to take the pram, will we?'

'Of course not, idiot.'

'That's the second time you've called me idiot, just for not knowing things *you* know.' She turned on him furiously. 'Well, at least I don't try and rape people.'

'Saying that only makes you a third kind of idiot. You know damn well I'd never rape anybody.'

'Whatever you thought you were doing, it was still rotten.'

'Are you telling me you didn't enjoy it?'

Her eyes smarted with tears, and blinking them back

recalled to her those other tears which had made him leave her alone. 'Would I have cried if I'd been enjoying it?'

'Yes, damn it, that's all in the game.' He seized her suitcase, and dumped it by the door. 'You must be getting a hell of a kick out of making me feel so guilty.'

'So you *do* feel guilty. That's something, I suppose.'

'Have you finished packing?'

'After you swore not to touch me.' She flung open the wardrobe and fetched out her flight-bag. 'After your big talk of how I'd been taken advantage of enough already.' She grabbed the bottle of mineral-water from her bedside table, and stuck it into the flight-bag. 'How I wasn't that kind of woman.' She cast about for the container with the sterilised bottles. 'Shows what your promises are worth when you take an idea in your head.'

'It wasn't my head that made me——' He broke off with a noise that sounded like a gulp. 'Give me a job to do, for heaven's sake, and let's get out of here.'

She was back at her desk, taking out her purse with English money, and her worryingly babyless passport. 'You could make Al up some bottles; he'll need at least two. . .'

'I've already done four.'

'So that's where the damned cointainer went——' She broke off, abashed at her own hectoring, ungracious tone.

But why should I be polite to him? she demanded of herself. I don't *feel* polite.

From the desk drawer, the white gold of the teething-ring winked up at her. It was the nearest she had to information on Al's name and birthdate. She shot a worried glance at Patrick, but he was stonily transferring his prepared bottles from the pram to the flight-bag, glaring down as if a glance in her direction might petrify him. She whipped a scarf round the teething-ring, dropped it in her pocket, and dashed to the bathroom.

'Have I packed enough nappies?' she called through the door. 'Heaven knows how many he'll get through.'

'I got in the ones you'd left out.' He sounded coldly satisfied. 'And I changed him just now.'

'So you can change a nappy.' She rinsed her hands, refusing to be impressed. 'I bet you haven't done the washing-up yet.'

'Damn the washing-up. Surely you're not taking this?'

She came out to find him waving the little blue teddy.

'Why not?' She seized it from him, unable to explain the sentimental impulse which had led her to stuff it in the outer pocket of the flight-bag. 'I don't expect a man like you to understand, but he loves this teddy.'

Which wasn't true; Al was too young even to know what it was. Trying to justify the lie, she hooked a finger through the red collar, and flourished the fluffy thing aloft.

'It's part of his routine. Change, play, feed, sleep——'

'I've already worked that out,' he interrupted. 'I just fed him, remember? Sorry,' he added bitterly, 'that's one of the best jobs, isn't it? But at least I also did my share of the chores.'

She let her short fingernail rub and rub against a roughness in the sewing where the bear's head met its body. Had he really taken so much to heart the things she'd said? A part of her wanted to give him credit, and thank him for his help.

That same cooler self-knowledge said that she wasn't behaving too well herself. 'Bossy-boots', he'd called her, and it struck a chord. She wouldn't for the world have let him know it, but that was downright polite compared to her brothers' name for her.

'All right, naggy-knickers.' Seventeen-year-old

David's irritated voice was suddenly there, astonishingly alive inside her aching head. 'But I'll get on with it my way, not yours.'

She eased out the bear's collar and minutely inspected the roughness in the neck. It had been badly sewn, or badly mended, or something. She couldn't really see to tell which; it was swimming around too much. What a fool she'd been, to offend Patrick's Leo pride with her Sagittarian bossiness. What a guaranteed way to get the worst out of him.

'It's all right, my darling, don't cry.' His arm was around her, one hand on her shoulder, the other smoothing the wet from her cheek. 'You'll be home soon.'

'Get away from me!' She sprang forward, fiddling with the teddy-bear so as not to have to show her brimming eyes. 'Up you come, my darling.'

She raised the sleeping Al, wrapped him in his shawl, and rested her cheek on his warm little head. That was better; she was back in control.

'I'll put this thing back, then.' He bit off the words as if he hated them, or her, or both, and returned the bear to the flight-bag pocket.

She felt the tears rising afresh at his renewed hostility. 'I hope you burped him properly.'

'That——' Patrick shouldered the flight-bag, and picked up the suitcase '—is one thoroughly burped baby.'

She nodded, knowing she'd only asked to make him pause. She had to take one farewell glance at that tranquil view of the next country. This afternoon it lay under whipped-cream clouds whose whiteness shone back at her from the river. The blue-white light brightened her reference-books and ring-binders and treasured pens, her pictures, the solitary armchair where she had fed Al, her lonely bed, the desk where she had so often

pushed back the loneliness by making the frescoes her
beloved friends. . .

'Come on.' But his voice was gentle now, and his hand
at her back only enough to urge her along the corridor.

Outside in the soot-tainted air, a soldier presented
arms at the wide-open monastery gates. He turned
ceremonially sideways to them, as no doubt he had been
taught, to indicate that the way was clear to the little
landing-stage. The *kapitan* waited in the tied-up boat—
the same smart fibreglass launch which had taken Claire
on her single visit to the city—and another officer stood
ready to untie its moorings.

'The commandant let me ride in this once,' she
observed as they drew near. 'He made a big favour of
it.'

The *kapitan* looked up, hearing what she'd said. 'He
make no more favours, Colonel Danev.'

'He's dead,' Patrick told her, passing the suitcase and
the flight-bag to the waiting *kapitan* and turning again to
Claire. 'Give me Al, while you get in.'

'D-dead?' She parted with the baby reluctantly, afraid
to let him out of her arms. 'In the fighting?'

'Student put knife here.' The *kapitan* showed with a
hand beneath his ear the pulse where jaw met neck. 'Is
very quick, much blood, no bullets. Many kill so, for
blood-feud.'

'Ugh.' Claire scrambled on board, seated herself on
the cushioned bench, and thankfully took her baby back
into her own charge. 'The things men do to each other.'

'Mikkimouse.' The *kapitan* meant the teddy-bear,
which he set on the bench beside her before turning a
key and bringing the engine to life. 'Is woman.'

'What?' Claire wasn't sure she'd heard right.

'Is woman who kill Colonel Danev. For her brother,
she say. Our women also can hate, Mees Fletchair.'

Claire wondered how any woman could possibly do

such a thing. Unbidden, a picture flashed in her mind of Donna Cortesi, all glitter and darkness as the star-flaming Queen of the Night, and something about the memory made her pull Al closer. Had Cortesi's grand-daughter really abandoned her child? Knowing that if he was found, and identified, he might be... She couldn't bear to think of it. How could any mother do that, whatever the emergency?

I never will, she silently promised the sleeping baby. If it's stay with you or leave without you, I stay.

Still, perhaps she was just the lucky one who was to get away easily. The lieutenant cast them off and saluted as they chugged away from the shore. The *kapitan* guided the boat into mid-river, explaining that the search of the monastery was to be completed only for form's sake— Cortesi was far more likely to be in the mountains. But they had now learnt enough of conditions in this troubled area to send back a report to the chief-of-staff in the capital, and that report must go by helicopter.

'Is no telephone neither,' he said sadly. 'All burnt up.'

Claire tried to thank him for letting her and Al ride along with the official messenger, but he waved it away.

'Is bargain with Meester Donofan.'

'Bargain?' She looked sharply at Patrick. 'What have you two been hatching between you?'

He didn't even tell her to mind her own business. The way he stared ahead, cold and impassive, she might never have spoken.

They were nearing the shore now, in air ever more sooty and acrid. Doing her best to shield Al's mouth and nose, avoiding Patrick's eye, and trying to forget the headache thudding at her temples, Claire hardly noticed how they were running slantwise upriver, well clear of the troubled town. It brought her a sense of relief, of happier things still existing in the world, to see the care and skill of the *kapitan* managing the boat.

'Is fine engine,' he answered when she complimented him. 'I like engines, Mees Fletchair.'

They pulled in at a willow-fringed, wooden landing-stage. Patrick leaped out and tied up, helped Claire ashore, and gestured to where the helicopter rose alien and metallic from among the grazing cattle of the riverside meadow.

She prepared to walk to it, but apparently they weren't ready yet. Leaving her on the landing-stage with Al and the luggage, the two men pushed through overhanging branches to where the June abundance of the leaves formed a thick curtain. It was the *kapitan* who parted this curtain, suddenly brilliant with excitement as a low-slung red car caught the sun among the wavering, water-green, leaf-green shadows.

'Hang on.' Patrick shouldered undergrowth aside with his usual lion's disregard, and moved a little up the slope from the river. 'It was this sycamore with the sawn-off branch.'

'What silly game are you playing now?' Claire demanded.

Nobody answered. The branch had been cut long ago, perhaps to stop it growing over the landing-stage. The tree stood higher than the river, but from its foot the tarred stump must still be above shoulder-level. That didn't bother Patrick, who found his way up to it as surely and easily as some damned great black cat. Now he was higher, out of sight in the leafy canopy which resounded with cheepings and chatterings and shrilling alarm-calls.

'Of all the times to go bird-nesting,' Claire muttered.

Nobody listened. The *kapitan* had produced an immaculate handkerchief, and he tenderly rubbed the car's paintwork until Patrick swung down, when he put away the handkerchief and sprang to reverent attention.

'They were still there.' Patrick waved a set of keys.

'You hid them in a *tree?*' Claire demanded in disbelief. 'You hid your car keys up a *tree?*'

Both men ignored her, but by now that was all she expected.

'Right.' Patrick's briskness seemed almost feverish. 'Five minutes to change into my own clothes, and it's all yours.'

Claire stared at him. 'You're giving your car away?'

He vanished among the willows without a word or a glance. Still, at least the *kapitan* felt some need to explain.

'Is for revolution, not for me,' he assured her, though he couldn't hide his delight. 'I drive back to headquarters.'

'But couldn't *he* do that?'

'With you? With baby?' The little man looked down at his polished army shoes. 'You must go quick, Mees Fletchair——'

'No, I mustn't,' Claire cut in wildly. 'I needn't go at all.'

'Yes, you do,' the hidden Patrick contradicted her.

'So you're still able to talk to me?' She turned to the rustling curtain of willow-boughs. 'I was beginning to think I'd gone invisible.'

'You're a foreigner with a home to go to, and you're going to it,' Patrick snapped from his hideaway. 'That'll leave us with one problem less here.'

'I'll solve my own problems.'

'Stop being silly.'

And he was right, she was being silly—sillier than he knew. She raised the sleeping baby so that she could set her lips to his cheek, his temple, the little complex whorl of his ear. For herself, she would never have accepted such a sacrifice from anybody, let alone from Patrick Donovan. But she hadn't only herself to think of, she had Al, who wouldn't be safe until he was right away

from here, where anyone at any time might connect him
with that privileged Tragana nursery.

'That's it, then.' Patrick pushed back to them, shrugging into an old, beautifully cut tweed jacket. 'Let's go.'

She stared at him. This, she realised, was the first
time that she had seen him in clothes of his own
choosing. This was how he presented himself to the
world, in heather-mixture tweeds which must have cost
somebody of lot of money, though maybe not him, to
judge by their age. They fitted his long, lean frame with
enormous distinction, and looked all the better for the
expensive cream-coloured shirt and the defiant paisley
tie which picked up the colours of the tweed.

'You. . .you look quite different.' She was conscious of
that chill of loneliness gripping her again in the hot, still
air. 'I. . . I never thought. . .'

She couldn't finish. How could she tell him she never
thought she could fancy a man who dressed as he did?
That she had taken him in those anonymous, dark,
casual clothes for one of her own sort—the easygoing,
wear-what-you-please students and academics who'd
been around her for the past few years?

And yet, this man was wearing what he pleased, too.
He wasn't following fashion—not in a suit of that age—
but he cared about his clothes; the shirt and tie and
those gleaming brogues showed that. What he'd suddenly become was his own man, who made up his own
mind about what he wore, how he lived, what he drove.

'Please, Patrick, please don't give up your car for me,'
she begged. 'There must be some other way——'

'There isn't,' he told her shortly. 'No petrol, no food,
no. . .no soap even, for God's sake. Come on.' He took
up the flight-bag with the bear still peering ludicrously
from its side-pocket, and turned to the *kapitan* with the
car keys laid out on his palm. 'You'll like driving her.
She's well named the Lynx.'

He whistled soundlessly as he parted with the keys,
but couldn't stay completely casual. When he had picked
up the case, he had to turn for one last look, one last
word to her new driver.

'If I find you've punished her brakes, I'll come looking
for you.'

'Please?' The little man was staring at the keys as if
he couldn't believe his luck.

'Nothing.' Patrick led the way to the helicopter.
'Introduce us to our pilot.'

The pilot spoke no English at all, so the introductions
were soon done as far as Claire was concerned. Once
more she faded into the background, this time literally
in a back seat where she hugged the sleeping baby
tight, to comfort both him and herself while they endured
the wretched clatter of the rotors and the sick sensation
of having left your stomach down there in the smoky
town.

Patrick and the pilot exchanged excited comments
which she couldn't understand about the devastation
below. She tried to take an intelligent interest, tried to
note how the gutted buildings on Volpes still
smouldered, but there on the other side lay Tragana
monastery, peach-warm in the late-afternoon light.

Tragana with her beloved frescoes. The library she
had grown to love almost as much. Her room, where the
stored-up peace and humility of the lay-brothers had so
often come to her aid.

And then she couldn't see anything; it was all swimming away from her. She thought she was crying, surely
she was crying, very quietly so that Patrick wouldn't
notice and feel he had to be nice to her again. But crying
didn't stop up your ears, did it? Crying didn't still the
clatter, and cover the world with darkness, and when
you blinked your eyes open it was still daylight after all,
but now you were above a forest with no river in sight.

On the next blink it wasn't a forest but a plain with
castles, villages, towns. And the next changed it all
again, to a city stretching over low hills, and beyond the
hills, an airport.

The airport. Dazed, Claire let herself be helped
through the mechanics of climbing out of the helicopter.
The pilot must have come here only to set her down—
he hardly waited for them all to get out before he'd
taken off again, high over that single-storey, glass-walled
building which she finally, muzzily recognised as the
departure-lounge. That was where they were; on the
parking-lot in front of the airport departure-lounge.

'Patrick!'

It was a woman, fair and sturdy and dressed for
travelling in a suit that looked as if it was made of brown
linen. She sounded overjoyed, climbing down from that
minibus to run towards them—or rather, towards
Patrick. When she reached him she did no more than
shake him warmly by the hand, but her eyes were
suspiciously wet.

'We didn't know if we'd ever see you again.' She spoke
too fast, but her naturally low voice sounded tightly
held-back, as if she was determined to stay cool. 'We
knew you must have gone to Tragana, but honestly
Patrick——' she stared accusingly up at him '—not to
say a word to a soul. . .'

'You know I'd never have got permission.' He stood
back. 'Daphne, this is Claire Fletcher—you know, the
Cortesi girl?'

'The Cortesi *scholar*,' Claire corrected him.

Only when it was out did she feel the smallness of it,
fussing over her dignity at a time like this. He didn't
answer at once, but bowed his head and closed his eyes
briefly in the bright sunlight. She had time to notice
those shadows under them, now etched deep into his
flesh, and then he was himself again.

'I beg your pardon. Now, can we get on?' He indicated their companion. 'This is Daphne Lane-Thomas, H.E.'s—the ambassador's—secretary. She'll look after you on the plane.'

'I will?' Daphne Lane-Thomas cast a startled glance from him to Claire, and seemed to see Al for the first time. 'Oh. Yes. Er—I didn't know you had a baby, Miss—er——'

Claire took a deep breath, and resigned herself to her new status as an unmarried mother. 'He was born in Tragana.'

She might as well get used to it; she'd have to repeat it often from now on. Including to her parents. Oh, dear; how would she put it to her parents? Her mother would understand at once, but what about her old-fashioned father, who had worked so hard to bring his own five children through the world?

'Oh.' Daphne Lane-Thomas was doing sums, as everybody would. 'Well—er——' She paused, and then, kindly and practical, put first things first. 'Of course I'll help with him. We've another baby on board, and a two-year-old. You'll be all right.'

She turned back to Patrick. 'The men had to stay at the embassy, packing documents.'

'Hell.' He looked at his watch. 'I suppose I'd better get back where I'm needed, then.' He glanced across to the minibus from which his colleague had appeared. 'Has the driver any further orders, or can he take me straight back?'

The woman—yes, she was an older woman, in her thirties perhaps—surveyed the car-park. 'Where's your Lynx?'

'Helping the revolution. Or so kapitan Todoresi says.'

'You mean, he's taken it?'

'Only in fair exchange.'

'Serves you right,' Daphne Lane-Thomas said briskly.

'And you might lose worse than that. H.E. says if you haven't been killed, he's going to personally disembowel you.'

Patrick sighed. 'Will it be one of his final warnings?'

She nodded. 'Maybe his last final warning. It's really high time you grew up, Patrick Donovan.'

Claire looked up, startled to hear her own words and feelings echoed so exactly. She found the dark blue eyes fixed on hers, as deep and unreadable as when she had first seen them.

'This time, I think maybe I have. Take care, Daphne.' He bent to brush the secretary's cheek with his lips. 'And. . .look after Claire, won't you?' He approached Claire, and stared down once more into her eyes. 'She's. . .she's worth looking after.'

Then his lips were on her cheek, too, leaving a little burning mark that stayed with her while he patted the baby.

'And so is he. Tell him about me some day, will you, Claire?'

She closed her eyes against the pain, and didn't care when the teddy-bear dropped from the side-pocket of the flight-bag. 'You speak as if you're never going to see us again.'

'Who knows? But anyway, it'll be different, won't it? If you've any sense—and you've plenty——' he picked up the teddy, and went on with a catch in his voice '—you'll tell his father, and give him a chance to marry you. He's not married already, is he?'

'N-no.' She remembered his own condescending half-proposal.

He glanced over to the minibus, which had just tooted twice. Daphne Lane-Thomas had gone to speak to the driver, and was now back with them, a little breathless, accepting the blue teddy-bear from Patrick without looking at it.

'He says he must get back at once.' She looked pleadingly at Patrick. 'They're still shooting. H.E. needs the bus to get the files to the Swiss embassy on the edge of town.'

'I'll be right there.' Patrick snapped to attention, all signs of fatigue vanished, and turned without another word to run to the minibus.

So it wasn't me leaving him, after all; it was him leaving me, Claire thought drearily, over and over again during that horrible plane-journey.

There was no stewardess, and the passengers were mostly silent. When Claire took her place with Al, the middle-aged bleached-blonde lady in the next seat closed long-suffering, blue-painted eyes as if this was the last straw, and kept them like that for the whole journey. Daphne Lane-Thomas was as good as her word, holding Al still to be changed, finding a place for used nappies, taking him while Claire prepared his feed in the little galley; but she was needed in many places.

'Little Janet's teething,' she hissed at one point. 'Poor love, it must be agony.'

Little Janet's crying set even placid Al off several times. The toddler kept escaping from his exhausted nanny to climb on to the lap of his dozing mother, who would scold him in a useless murmur. The light glared, the engine droned, the whole bleak, miserable world surged forward and retreated like waves on the seashore, and then they'd arrived somewhere.

London? Wasn't that English all these people were talking? Yes, English. Flashing lights, thrusting microphones, stupid questions about how they all felt, making Al cry yet again. No wonder Daphne was growing impatient, pleading for common sense, pushing one man aside.

'Nearly over, love,' she shouted above Al's exhausted

wailing as they battled into the terminal. 'Have you somewhere to go? Because if not——'

'Mother!' Claire called, unable to believe her eyes.

As slender and lively as a woman half her age, Lesley Fletcher ducked under the barrier and darted across the arrivals-hall. A smaller figure followed her; ten-year-old Matthew. A policeman made to stop them but she dodged round one side of him, Matthew the other, and when the man saw where they were heading he nodded with a sympathetic grin.

'Oh, my darling!' She wrapped her daughter in a tearful, unbelieving embrace which somehow, used as she was to babies, included the still-wailing Al as a matter of course. 'Matthew, go and find your father; he's here somewhere. . .'

She turned back to Claire without waiting to see if her son had obeyed. 'It's been in the news for days, your Tragana,' she choked, hardly making sense. 'We tried and tried to find out about you, nobody knew, nobody seemed to care. . .' She turned to look back across the barrier, searched face after face in the throng. 'Where can Piers have go to? He said we mustn't hope too much. . . What's this?'

For the first time she became aware of Al as something extra to her daughter, something not quite expected. Claire met the dark grey eyes so like her own, and nodded without a word.

'Darling!' said Lesley. 'What is your father going to say?'

CHAPTER SIX

'A! BA,' Al called from his cot in the bed-sitting-room.

Claire put down her pen. 'Tea-time, already?'

Yes, it was five o'clock, and at some point she'd switched on the neon strip here in the kitchen-diner. Beyond the sink, the sky behind the leafless trees of the Grove had gone from grey to pewter, to street-lit black.

She flicked the blue-striped curtains shut, and closed the roll-top desk over her precious papers. They'd had trouble moving this desk down here from her mother's study, and its scuffed bulk crowded the tiny space, but she never ceased to be grateful for it. Now that she was weaning Al, food flew everywhere, but none had yet found its way on to her thesis, her drawings, or her photographs.

'All right, cup-cake.'

She went into the bed-sitting-room, scarcely bigger than the kitchen-diner, and picked Al up. He crowed, and hit her with his much-eaten blue bear.

'He loves this bear,' she'd told Patrick seven months ago, and since then it had come true.

'Bully.' She flapped a towel one-handed over the sunflower-patterned divan, and set him down on it. 'It's no good kicking; this nappy's got to be changed.'

The deed done, she put him into the berry-red woollies which her sister had sent from Canada. ''Cos this is January.' She rubbed his cheek with her noise. 'Jan-u-ar-y. Co-o-old. Brrr.'

Al flailed about him with Ted, until she fitted him into the harness of the doorway-swing. That produced an expectant hush, followed by gurgles of delight as she set him safely bouncing on the thick, elastic ropes.

'Ride a cock horse to Banbury cross. . .'

But already he was away, working the swing for himself. She stayed to watch, loving his vigorous kicks and excitedly waving arms, his shouts and chuckles as he settled to his own rhythm. They reminded her, as Al so often had done in the past seven months, of Patrick Donovan; his restless energy, his love of life, his deftness with any task he set himself to.

Had Al inherited those qualities? Who knew? Her mother was convinced that he took after her side of the family.

'He's got my father's very eyes,' she'd said only yesterday, when her busy day allowed her to look in. 'His very look.'

The odd thing was, Claire could see it too. Grandfather Dai, pottering at the Cardiff plumbing business in spite of every loving effort to make him retire, had exactly this lively bearing. Yes, and exactly Al's jovial skill in getting his own way.

But then, so had Patrick. To still the familiar ache, she busied herself at the little fridge. For that matter she bet Adam had it—in Paradise and after.

It paid to get Al hungry. By the time she'd scrambled the eggs, he was ready to let most of his share be put in his mouth, and none came back into the pelican bib. Her overall suffered only when he scored a direct hit on the spoon with his fist.

'Messy boy.' She stretched to the sink for the sponge.

That was one thing about this tiny flat above what had been the stables; everything was to hand. Wiping Al with one hand, clearing away with the other, she scarcely had to move her feet, even to answer the phone in the other room.

'Daphne!' she exclaimed, delighted to hear the voice

of the woman who had become a close friend. 'Can you drop in this evening, then?'

'So you'll be home.' Daphne sounded oddly reluctant. 'I thought this might be one of your evenings at the Tech.'

'That's tomorrow. It's Mum who's on tonight.'

'Will I be able to use her parking-slot?'

How like Daphne to think ahead. Claire smiled, honouring such sturdy reliability. What a treasure Jim Sloane had won when, last September, he'd made Daphne Lane-Thomas his wife.

'Is Jim playing squash?'

'Er—well, no. As a matter of fact he's—er—we were both going to stay home and watch telly.'

'You haven't quarrelled?'

'Of course not. Well, not exactly; he isn't home yet. . . Look, you will be on your own, won't you?'

'Like I said, Mum's out. David's on A-level homework as usual.' Also the least Al-besotted of the family, Claire might have added. 'Dad might look in at bath-time, and Matt if he's——'

'Can you stop them?'

'What?' Claire wasn't sure that she'd heard correctly. 'You don't usually mind my family.'

'This isn't a usual visit.'

'So something *is* wrong. Are you in trouble?'

'Not in the least, everything's fine. It's only. . . Listen, what's the soonest you can get Al down and out?'

Claire glanced at her impatient son, and then at his swing still fixed in the kitchen doorway. Another half-hour of it would have him asleep before he reached his cot, but Daphne had never asked such a thing before. Unlike Jim, who said the only good baby was a sleeping baby, she generally revelled in Al's bedtime.

'An hour should do it.'

'Good. That'll give me time to get Jim home, and explain.'

'Explain?'

'Between seven and half-past, then.'

A quick call to the main house brought Matt to the phone. Puzzled but co-operative, he agreed to persuade their father not to visit this evening, and Claire put Al back in the swing to get him good and tired.

She was always grateful for Daphne's visits. Seven months ago, she had decided not to return to university to finish her thesis, but to stay here at home in the Grove where her parents were being so helpful. Daphne did something to fill the place of her sister, Linda, two years married to her Canadian farmer.

'Though thank heaven Linda's twins came when they did,' Claire reflected as she lowered Al into the baby-bath which she kept in the shower-stall. 'I wonder if they'll ever find out how marvellous their timing was?'

Last spring, while she was studying for her master's degree at Durham, her Cortesi scholarship had come at very short notice. Her parents, frantically packing for Linda's great event, had wanted to miss their flight and see her off to Tragana, but she wouldn't let them.

Instead, she had said her goodbyes on the phone, and started her own journey from Newcastle airport. So nobody here had seen her during her supposed pregnancy. Her reappearance with Al had caused her parents much concern, but no suspicion; they never doubted that he was hers.

'I won't pretend I like what you've done,' Claire's mother frequently announced, 'but after the misery of having to leave Lin and the twins. . .' Here, she always cuddled her grandson, who was always within reach, before going on. 'Only, why didn't you *tell* us, darling?'

'And what would you have done? Cancelled the air-tickets, after all your trouble in getting them?' From about the fourth time, Claire had it word-perfect. 'Called Lin, and told her not to have the babies till I was all sorted out?'

'But to go off so pregnant, to somewhere so difficult.'

'It had to be then or not at all,' Claire would point out. 'And I wasn't going to lose my only chance to see the frescoes.'

'As if that mattered, when. . . Honestly!' At this point, Lesley Fletcher always kissed Al. 'Who'd have children?'

It was a small price to pay for her parents' support, this often-repeated argument. So was the other about Al's Australian 'father', departed and not answering letters. Claire had long given up being surprised at the skill and fluency of her own lies. Nowadays she almost believed it herself—that Tom Evans was out there somewhere, backpacking his way home to Tasmania.

'I'll get to him some day,' Piers Fletcher would huff and puff. 'I'll make him face his responsibilities.'

But he was far too much of a homebody to make such a journey lightly. He'd grown up in this Clapham Regency crescent long before it became a fashionable street. His daily journey to his bank in Streatham was all the travelling he ever wanted, and he was only too happy to see his daughter and grandson settled in what had been built as the coachman's quarters.

'I'll manage,' Claire assured him when he worried about the smallness of the flat. 'I know how lucky I am to have it.'

She insisted on paying them rent, teaching art part-time at her mother's technical college. Any hours she could manage from that and from caring for Al—like these precious Wednesday afternoons—were reserved for her thesis.

It was a busy life, which only felt empty when she remembered Patrick. She did that as little as possible, though still a lot more than she wanted to. Like now, settling Al in his cot—weren't his eyes an unusually dark blue? So dark blue that they looked black in this electric light? And wasn't that a hint of a one-sided smile as he tried to charm away bedtime?

'This is silly. You're a Fletcher now.' She gave him Ted and kissed him goodnight. 'Whatever else you are, it'll have to wait till you've grown a bit.'

Which brought another flood of memories, this time disguised as imaginings of how he'd grow. Would he wear silly Leo underwear? Eagerly learn whatever she could tell him about the Tragana frescoes? Hide his car keys up a tree?

No, only Patrick would do something as far-out as that. He must have had to climb that sycamore in nothing but his trunks—no wonder they were giving him trouble when she first met him. He was lucky to have kept them on at all.

She sometimes wondered bleakly if she'd ever forgotten a single word, a single touch that had passed between them. As she turned off the bed-sit's top light to encourage Al's sleep, tidied her divan and plumped its cushion-covered backrest-pillows, she found that she was quarrelling anew.

How could you jump on me like that? Treating me like an object, with no feelings of my own?

And a ghostly Patrick answered in her head. It was only because of the way you tried to order me about.

You talked of marriage as a favour you might do me.

You threw it back in my face before I could work out what I meant by it.

Oh, dear. Why couldn't they start again, re-run the whole scene like one of those film out-takes that went wrong?

'Because it wouldn't change, however often you tried it. He's a Leo who wants all his own way.' She ran hot

water for the dishes. 'And I'm a Sagittarius who won't—
I mean wouldn't have—put up with his nonsense.'

How difficult to accept, even after all these months,
that Patrick was now a part of her past. When she
thought of never seeing him again, she wanted to open
the window and shout his name into the murmuring
London evening. He'd be out there in it some time,
home from his posting, preparing for another. Maybe,
even, now and again, thinking of her?

Thank heaven Daphne was coming. And with something on her mind, so that perhaps she wouldn't talk of
Patrick as she so often did. Claire had come to dread
those stories of his escapades, and yet always had to
listen, fascinated.

'You can't help liking him,' was one of Daphne's
favourite comments, always followed by, 'if only he'd
grow up a little.'

And then she'd shake her head, and recall some tale
she hadn't recounted yet. How he'd committed protocol
sin by walking out of a reception ahead of his own
ambassador, rather than shake hands with the epaulet-
ted commander-in-chief of the Forget-me-nots. How he'd
torn down what he had called a 'great God Cortesi'
poster under the affronted nose of the Forget-me-not
who was fixing it to the wall outside her flat. How he'd
taken his early-morning jog through forbidden Kalavesi
parkland, and come back with a bright blue cap to prove
it.

How he'd flouted all sense and reason by falling for
the dictator's granddaughter.

'He denied it, but we could all see it,' Daphne would
shrug. 'Whenever she sang, there he'd be, alone in the
stage-box.'

Claire had to ask. 'But didn't Cortesi object?'

'It's my belief she had her grandfather just where she
wanted him. In fact,' Daphne speculated, 'I always

thought she must have inherited a lot of his. . .' She frowned, her honest, round eyes perplexed. 'It's not a word I use much, but I can only call it his. . .*evil*.'

'You know him?'

'Of course not! But I met Donna a couple of times, at official receptions.' Daphne shivered. 'I. . . I didn't like her.' Clearly this was one of her well-bred understatements. 'I didn't exactly wish her ill, but I was glad when she went—wherever she did go.'

Tragana?

'It was after Patrick went to Paris for the weekend, and it turned out she'd been there, too,' Daphne added. 'Maybe Cortesi decided enough was enough.'

Or sent her away to have her baby in secret?

It wasn't just idle speculation, Claire thought, as she dried the dishes and put them away. One day Al would want to know who he was, and he had a right to some answers. That was why—the only reason why, she hastily assured herself—she'd sunk her own pride, and written to Patrick again and again.

The doorbell put an end to that particular useless fuming. Claire whipped the overall from her old jeans and sober grey sweater and hung it by the tea-towel. Then she switched off the white kitchen light, closed the kitchen door, unhooked the swing and pushed it under the cot, and was ready to take the two paces needed to open the front door.

'Is he asleep?' Daphne hissed, arm raised to let a ceiling-mobile of little sparkling umbrellas dance in the brisk wind of the outside stone steps.

'No need to whisper; I've got him used to noise.'

Daphne, who already had a well-appointed nursery for her own eagerly awaited child, tried to hide her disapproval. 'Will this amuse him, do you think?'

'I'm sure he'll love it. Thank you.'

Claire accepted it with pleasure, though wondering

where she could hang the mobile in her tiny space. She ushered her friend into the crowded little bed-sitting-room, where Daphne cooed over the sleeping Al, and unwound a lavender scarf from brown tweeds.

She didn't remove it. 'No coffee, thanks.'

'Aren't you staying?' Claire asked in disappointment.

'I told you, Jim and I——'

Daphne broke off, and glanced at the little casement window with its sunflower curtains. It might almost have been a hunted look, but also exasperated. Puzzled, Claire offered an opening.

'You're sure you and Jim haven't quarrelled?'

'We haven't, but he says we might. He's given me one hour, door to door.' Daphne sounded surprised, and pleased, to find her husband putting his foot down. 'And it took me twenty minutes getting here, so I'd better—er——'

'Well? You'd better what?' Claire settled on the bed, laying the mobile on her pillow. 'Won't you even sit down?'

'I suppose so.' Daphne lowered herself on to the front edge of the armchair, and fiddled with the single strand of good pearls which hung on her lavender jersey. 'You can't help liking him, that's the trouble.'

Claire jerked to attention, then realised how she'd misunderstood. 'I should think so, seeing as he's your husband.'

'Not Jim, silly.' Daphne straightened, folded her hands, and drew a careful breath. 'Patrick Donovan came to tea.'

Everything suddenly went a long way off. The cot on the right, the kitchen door on the left, the bookcase in the corner with the yellow-shaded lamp, the low-burning gas fire; all dwindled to the tiny, misshapen image that you might see in a crystal ball. And why was that gas

fire popping so, and when had that battery wall-clock
started ticking so loudly?

'So he's home?' Claire croaked across the thunderous
ticking.

'On leave between postings. He hasn't been able to
take any leave for two years.' Daphne spoke too fast,
running away from something. 'So he has about two
months to come. He'll be going up to his folks in
Scotland, if you don't——' She stopped, closed her
mouth tight, opened it, and took a slow breath. 'He
wants to see you.'

'But. . .then why didn't he. . . We're in the book,'
Claire stammered, trying to make sense. 'Why didn't he
just call?'

Was it fear, this churning in her stomach? Was it joy
making her head suddenly ready to float away like a
balloon?

'He. . .he said——' Daphne stared down at the bright
rag rug '—he didn't want you hanging up on him. Or
banging the door.'

'As if I'd ever be so rude! So. . .so ungrateful!'

'He seems to think you've reason to be angry with
him.' Daphne clearly found it hard to speak of such
private feelings. 'And seeing as you didn't answer his
letters——'

'What letters? And why did he never answer mine?'

Daphne raised her eyes in a 'how-did-I-get-into-this?'
manner. 'Five minutes in a helicopter, and you reached
this stage?'

'What stage?'

Daphne shrugged. 'It's your business, of course.'

Claire stared at the popping gas fire. She simply
hadn't realised until now that one of the attractions of
this English lady-friend was her restraint. Daphne asked
no awkward questions, so she was told no lies. Until
now, it had somehow been taken for granted between

them that Patrick had found her and Al somewhere in the city of Tragana, and brought them to the the airport, without having much time to get acquainted.

'It was a bit more than five minutes,' she managed at last.

'So I gather.'

'Not much more.'

'Enough for him start work on me when he found that I knew you. He asked. . .' Daphne paused, reticent as ever '. . .if you'd married Al's father. When he found you hadn't, nothing would do but my coming here. Only Patrick Donovan,' she added grimly, 'could make me turn out on a winter evening that I'd meant to spend with my husband.' Her pleasure slightly underlined the last word. 'He even talked Jim round to it. You can't help liking him.'

Claire raised her eyebrows. 'If only he'd grow up?'

'That's just it.' The other woman sounded bewildered. 'It could be that he has.'

Claire was astonished at her own dismay. She almost shouted aloud that she didn't *want* Patrick grown up. She wanted him being Patrick, doing crazy things and kind things and funny things and stupid, maddening, inexcusable. . .

'I suppose that's good news,' she managed at last.

'You knew about his outstanding bravery while the embassy was under fire, back in June?'

Claire didn't. She'd never asked for news of Patrick; only gobbled up what crumbs she was given. But her friend took the answer for granted.

'Of course you do; that's just Patrick being Patrick. Well, because of it, H.E.—the ambassador?' she interjected, with an enquiring glance to make sure that she was understood. 'H.E. gave him one more chance. And would you believe it? He's been a model diplomat ever since.'

'It must have helped that the Forget-me-nots are gone,' Claire commented wryly. 'And he's been living in the middle of exciting developments.'

'Also, it's only seven months,' her friend agreed. 'Exactly what I told him myself. But he says he means to keep it up.'

'And you think he will?'

'Anybody's guess.' The smooth, fair head shook, but more in wonder than with its usual definite opinion. 'Still, there it is. He particularly asked me to tell you, and I have.'

'And why,' Claire began, not daring to guess, 'did he particularly want *me* told?'

'If *you* don't know, how d'you expect *me* to?' Daphne glanced at her watch. 'My twenty minutes are up. So you're willing to see him?'

'I'd never not have been,' Claire rushed on, confused but knowing exactly what she meant. 'After all he did for me.'

'He seems to think differently, but you can sort that out for yourselves.' Daphne rose, and threw back her scarf in her usual businesslike manner. 'He says if you want to see him again, you're to open your window.'

'What?' Claire found she, too, was on her feet, wanting to sing, to laugh, to cry. 'He's here?'

'He insisted on coming with me.'

And now he was waiting, out there in the street beyond the sunflower curtains. It was all Claire could do not to rush over and wrench them apart, leaving her visitor to see herself out. She glanced at Al, making sure he was under all his blankets.

'But it's freezing out there.'

'That——' Daphne jingled her car keys '—is *his* problem.'

'And I'm to lean out of my window like. . .like Juliet?'

'Heaven spare me a balcony scene!' Daphne glanced

at the jewelled watch that Jim had given her for
Christmas. 'I've done what he asked, and now I'm off.'

Claire couldn't help it; she had to fling her arms
around her friend. She felt at once the awkwardness, the
resistance which held that embraces were for children
and close relations, but she must hug somebody or burst.

'You'll be careful, won't you?' Daphne stood back,
frowning. 'I'd hate to think. . .' She glanced at the cot.

'You mean, once is bad enough.' Claire was babbling,
bubbling, not making any sense, and it didn't matter.
'Twice starts to look like carelessness?'

'That's not at all. . . Oh, this is impossible.' Daphne
flicked back her scarf. 'Call if you need me. I'll be round
again soon.'

Claire opened the outside door, and switched on the
outside light. 'That'll be great.'

Everything would be great from now on. The light
made rainbows through the dimness, the door opened
on a wind that was as sweet as ice-cream, closed with a
music that you couldn't stay to hear because you had to
get to this window, tear back the curtains, and open it,
open it, open it. . .

There he was, striding away up the street. The fine
head sported a knitted cap pulled rakishly forward, the
wide shoulders a vast striped scarf, but you couldn't ever
mistake the lean height, the swagger, the easy grace
unhindered by that thick winter sweater.

But why is he walking in that direction? she wondered.
Doesn't he know where I live?'

It was all right; he'd stopped. He must have ears like
a wild creature, like the lion of his birth sign, to have
heard her casement opening. He sprung round in one
lithe movement and ran back, the blur of his face alert
while his soft-clad feet pounded the uneven pavement.
He reached the stone steps to the flat as Daphne pattered
down them, lifted her from them, whirled her, and

carried her protesting to her waiting car. She opened it, and straightened to address Claire at the window.

. 'Maybe he hasn't changed so much, after all.'

Patrick ignored her, looking up with black, intent eyes. 'You'll let me in?'

Only when she heard the deep voice did Claire realise that he hadn't said a word till now. It was as if he'd been saving it, had sworn some mad vow not to speak again until he could speak to *her*.

To me, her heart sang over the rustling trees and the distant traffic noises. To me. He wants to talk to *me*.

Aloud, she only called softly, 'I'll let you in.'

He at once took charge of the door of Daphne's car. While she arranged herself within it he removed his cap, placed it over his heart, and and swept her a deep bow.

'Honey-child, I owe you one.'

Claire giggled. Only Patrick would get away with calling the sensible, efficient, distance-keeping Daphne *that*.

'Yes.' The sharp tones came out slightly muffled from behind the wheel. 'And don't ever give me cause to regret it.'

'If I ever do, honey-child——' he closed the car, and raised his voice a little to be heard through it '——take me to the zoo, and feed me to the polar bears.'

'The conceit of the man!' Daphne had wound down her window. 'Polar bears are choosy. I'll feed you to the crocodiles; they'll eat anything.'

Her engine sang into life. Patrick leaped to the little wall of the area railings, clung to them with one hand and waved his cap in the other. The car nosed along the curve of the suddenly beautiful crescent, past silver-edged trees, jade and amethyst and amber-curtained windows, pearl and cornelian parked cars, to edge into the bright, murmuring high street like a modest soul being admitted to heaven.

No; heaven was here. Heaven was closing this window, crossing the little room, opening this door before he could reach it, while his feet still pounded the steps. Heaven was standing here in the entrance, between warm room and cold street, between yellow house-light and blue street-light, until the dear arms gathered you close and you could feel, in the wide chest under all these unfamiliar swaths of wool, a heartbeat as strong as your own.

'Will you marry me, Claire? Will you?'

A disapproving bark exploded from the street-lit foot of the steps. Claire and Patrick sprang apart, but that didn't satisfy next-door's over-bred saluki. It barked again.

'Bad boy, Timmy. Bad, bad boy. Sorry, Claire.'

'Th-that's all right.'

Next-door Serena, fair hair loose over her tracksuit, urged her pet off the steps. 'People have a perfect right to—er——' she made an embarrassed pause '—to, to *stand* at their own front door if they want to.'

She bade them a hasty, cool goodnight. It wasn't hard to make out what Serena thought about neighbours who clung to male visitors in public, doubly lit from house and street and raised above the pavement as if on a stage.

Claire wondered if she'd heard that outrageous proposal of marriage. Then her own maternal ears picked up the little noise of Al glopping and sighing in his sleep, and she broke away from Patrick to the cot.

'Do come inside, and shut the door.'

She was ordering him about the minute they'd met, but first things first. Al was fine, just turning over and still covered by all his blankets, but thank heaven for it, when she'd let all their expensively gained warmth out of window and door. She stooped to turn the gas-fire up full as Patrick went to the cot.

'He's asleep.' He sounded disappointed.

'If he weren't——' Claire stood up, and found herself jammed against the armchair '—you'd know about it.'

'Oh, well. Plenty of time. . .' He, too, had straightened, and now stared down at her. 'Did I propose to you back there?'

She had to smile as she took in his absurd height. Whatever would the old coaching gentry have done if their coachman had been this big? His head wasn't exactly jammed against the ceiling, he didn't exactly fill the place like a cork in a bottle, but that was what he made you think of.

'Did I?' he persisted.

She nodded. 'Don't you remember?'

'I don't remember a thing except being with you again, after months of. . . Damn!' He grabbed off his cap and flung it onto the divan, his black hair rumpled and a little longer than when she'd last seen him. 'And damn, and double-damn!'

'It's all right.' But she couldn't help the disappointment from sharpening her voice. 'I won't hold you to it.'

The cap was dark blue, she noted, and so was the scarf he'd just unwound and dropped on top of it. When he threw himself down beside them, Daphne's umbrella-mobile tumbled from the pillow under the impact of his weight, and sparkled crazily on top of the scarf.

Claire pointedly stayed on her feet. 'Do sit down.'

'Eh? Oh.' He leaped up, only his cat-like grace keeping him from colliding with the cot. 'I'm sorry, I've had nothing but men around me for——' He broke off. 'Come on, Claire. This isn't you, fussing about protocol.'

'Isn't it?' she fenced, still trying to deal with his taking back that proposal. 'How do you know?'

'Because you. . .because I. . . Hell!'

She never did know whether it was her move or his which brought them together. Whichever it was, it didn't

take much in the tiny space, and the other of them,
whichever that was, responded at once.

They were together again like magnet and pin, rock
and limpet, envelope and stamp. That was how Claire
felt, as if some great outside force had brought her to
him and was holding her to him, stirring all those
memories she'd stopped believing and all those dreams
she'd never understood.

And they were all true. It had been here all the time,
this closeness, this one-ness. Just as it had been in her
dreams, his mouth tasted of cloves and her fingers in his
hair released the scent of rosemary. Just as in her
dreams, he loosened her own hair without taking his lips
from hers, buried one of his hands in it as it fell round
her shoulders, followed its heavy length to the middle of
her back, then left it to press her close.

And yes, this was in her dreams, too. The fire within
her leaped and surged, longing to engulf this other male
flame, longing to taste and become one with it. . . Her
dreams had always ended here, in worry and shame,
just as this waking dream did now with her breaking
free.

'This is silly.' She pushed back her burden of hair,
pushed back her rebellious body. 'We've hardly said a
word to each other. . . What are you doing?'

Swinging her off her feet was what he was doing. And
if she couldn't fight him now, she certainly wouldn't be
able to in another minute or two.

'Let me go!' She fastened one hand in his hair and
beat his chest with the other. 'If you aren't the most. . .'

'Save it.' He kissed her ear.

'Put me *down*, you———'

She broke off in despair. Every contact of her flesh
with his was like sparks on tinder. His lips on her ear
had sent the flame from her head to her heart, and she
was helpless. *Che sarà sarà*, her mind sang, while her

hand rose from his chest and caressed his strong neck, and her other hand that had been pulling his hair explored the outlines of his head, and the scent of rosemary that showered down on her.

'You see?' His lips traced a hot track to her cheek. 'This is why I was in such a hurry to. . .' He stopped, raised his head away from her, and drew in a long, ragged breath. Then he dumped her in the armchair. 'To sit down,' he finished hoarsely, himself dropping back on to the bed.

The sparkly umbrellas, tangled amid their strings and sticks, slid to the floor. Claire followed their slide with her eyes, trying to hypnotise herself back to the cool, sensible everyday creature she really was.

Patrick had pulled a massive, gaudy handkerchief from a side-pocket of his smooth tweed trousers. With it came a folded paper, which he seized eagerly as on a talisman.

'Here it all is. I wrote it in the plane coming home, and I've been going through it ever since.' He opened the folds with such haste that two of them tore.

'Number one,' he read out, 'apologise for. . .' He looked up, clearly preferring to ad-lib '. . .for what nearly happened, back in Tragana. And, could you keep as far from me as possible, please?' He swallowed hard, the dark, dark eyes refusing hers. 'Otherwise it still might.'

'I see.' Claire was relieved to hear her own voice, only a little weaker and more hesitant than usual. 'You're. . .you're really sorry for that?'

As he was for having asked her to marry him.

'I wrote three times, apologising. Once to Durham.' He dropped his sheet of paper on top of his scarf, and pulled a diary from a back-pocket. 'Didn't you say you were at Durham University? That's what I've got here, along with every other little clue I could remember. . .'

'I didn't go back,' she interrupted, and nodded at sleeping Al. 'Things aren't so easy now.'

'I thought of that.' He consulted his diary again. 'So I sent the other two to the Grove, London.'

She choked on a nervous giggle. 'I wonder how many London streets are called the Grove?'

'I hoped the Post Office would keep trying.'

'You're sure your letters made it across the frontier?'

'They'd do that all right, in the diplomatic bag.'

'I sent mine direct to your embassy.'

'Then I thought of getting a mate of mine to. . . You what?' He dropped the diary on the rest of his belongings, and spoke as if he wanted to believe, but couldn't. 'So you did write?'

'Three times.' She, too, was trying to master her longing to believe. 'You didn't get them?'

'If you sent them through the ordinary mail, I wouldn't. The only stuff that's been reaching us——'

'I didn't apologise, like you,' she told him with difficult honesty. 'But maybe I should have. For. . .for being so bossy.'

'We were both tired out of our minds.' He reached down by his feet for the little glittery umbrellas, and started untangling them. 'What I want to do is start again, properly.'

'P-properly?'

The little umbrellas floated free, dancing at the end of their strings. He took up his piece of paper.

'Number two, give flowers,' he read aloud. 'Three, ask out to dine.'

'That's me, you'd be asking out to dine?' she repeated, wanting to be sure.

He nodded, intent on his luck-bringing list. 'Four, various outings with Al. Five, meet parents and make them like me.'

'They'll like you,' she put in, Daphne's favourite

comment on him ringing through her mind. 'But—er—
Patrick,' she said, as she recalled the second part of it,
'have you grown up?'

She wasn't sure what she wanted him to answer. She
certainly wasn't prepared to see him crumple that silly,
hopeful, heavenly paper and throw it across the room.
She wanted to jump up and rescue it, smooth it out to
put in her souvenir-box along with Al's first bootees.

'I'd like to have thought so,' he growled, 'but it only
took seeing you, being near you, to ruin it all.'

'It's ruined? Already?'

'Well, isn't it? That was supposed to come right at the
end.' He twirled and twirled the sparkly umbrellas. 'In
Kew Gardens, or in Kent among the apple blossom. It
was going to be spring by then.' He looked up at her at
last. 'When I finally asked you to marry me.'

CHAPTER SEVEN

Rain squalled on the windscreen. The wipers cleared their half-circles, which at once blurred as badly as before. Clear-and-blur, clear-and-blur, they swished in hypnotic rhythm across the advancing headlights of the northbound carriageway and the retreating tall-lights of the southbound. Claire fought off sleep, savouring every moment of this cosy togetherness which could last for such a little time longer.

'So this is March going out like a lamb.' She slipped her feet from their suede brogues, and flexed them in the carpeted warmth. 'I wonder if Al's got that tooth yet?'

She had wondered this aloud at least once every waking hour throughout the whole weekend. Patrick would have been entitled to show a little boredom with the question, but he didn't. For her, he would suspend his Leo scorn of small excitements like Al's first tooth, and care about it because she did.

'Your mother said she could feel it this morning, when you rang.' He stayed relaxed at the wheel, never taking his eyes off the road. 'It's probably all over and done with by now.'

'But I want to be *there* for it. . .' She trailed off, ashamed of her selfishness. 'Oh, well. How far to London?'

'Depends what you call London,' he answered with remembered affection. 'My mother thinks it starts at Milton Keynes.'

She smiled, trying to forget her own nagging problem which wouldn't be put off much longer. 'Your parents aren't a bit as I expected.'

125

He didn't ask what she'd expected; he was too busy
overtaking a tanker. This was another of the things that
she liked about him—his skill as a driver. Remembering
the sporty Lynx he'd given up on Tragana, she'd
expected him to be too showy on the road. But no, he
chose this sleek Benevola for its family weight and
comfort, and drove it considerately and with absolute
concentration.

Which was good to know at the moment, with conditions so difficult. She resolved to stop distracting him,
and to try instead to work out what she should do. She'd
been using this weekend in Erlington as an excuse for
putting it all out of her mind. Now the weekend was
over, and it was decision time.

Did she tell Patrick the truth about Al, or not?

Put like that, it answered itself. Her truth-loving
Sagittarian conscience stung her with a hundred arrows.
She couldn't live a whole lifetime with a lie like this.

And yet. . .the blood-feud? Donna Cortesi? Only last
week, Patrick had casually mentioned hearing that she
had escaped to Vienna, where she was continuing her
singing career as best she could.

'Not that it's much, without her grandfather to back
her.'

'You mean she isn't really that good a singer?' Claire
had asked with sinking heart.

'Dedicated, beautiful, great stage presence,' he
summed up. 'But she hasn't the range. And there's a
coldness. . .' He paused, careful as always when speaking
of his old love. 'Let's just say, she's not good at the more
vulnerable rôles.'

'She might be, now she's poor.'

'Donna, poor?' Patrick laughed. 'She's living with one
of Vienna's old nobility. And she'll leave him as soon as
something better turns up.'

'She's had her misfortunes.'

'They'll only have made her tougher.'

'Not all of them. . .'

But Claire couldn't say any more, not casually and never to him, of all people. Some day, in the right time and place, she would have to, and then wait to see if it broke her life wide open.

Meanwhile, he couldn't know, and she couldn't tell him, that Donna Cortesi had lost a child.

Until he turned up again, I never needed to think about it, she reflected. It had all started to seem like a dream.

But Al was real enough. He would be at least as real to the woman who bore him, who must still feel his loss like an unhealing wound. How she must hate herself for having left him, not knowing whether he'd even survived. And if her singing career wasn't prospering, that left her all the more time to wonder about her baby, and maybe try to find out what had become of him.

Vienna's a lot nearer Tragana than the Grove is, Claire thought with that familiar weight in her stomach. She only has to meet kapitan Todoresi, or any of his men, to know it was me who took Al away.

She had long since decided that, if Al's mother ever came for him, he must go to her. Only, how would Patrick feel about that? If Al was his—if, if, if—she sometimes felt her mind going round and round, back and forth like these windscreen-wipers.

But if he's fathered a child, he'll want to know about it.

The stubborn truth persisted in her mind, stronger than ever now that she knew Patrick so well. One of the many things she'd learnt about him in the past two months was how, even at his wildest, he would never had dodged any consequence of his own actions.

And he always cared about people. Donna Cortesi's strange, strained life must have given endless reasons for hiding her pregnancy, but if Patrick had known about it, and known too that he was the father, he'd have done everything possible to help.

He'd have married her. Claire faced it miserably. And you can't go on hiding it from him. You can't be that false.

Up till now, she'd been able to put the whole problem to the back of her mind. Life was so busy. Patrick was so busy, using his two months' leave to work through his crazy list and haul her along with him, laughing and protesting and loving him, always loving him.

Even thinking of that list made her smile. She'd often longed to touch his hand, or stroke his cheek, or kiss the corner of his mouth where it turned up in that self-mocking grin. But he'd given his orders, and she had learnt to obey. Until his list was completed, she mustn't come near him, or touch him even by accident.

Meeting her parents had been his item five. However, the senior Fletchers, made resolute by their anger with Al's mythical father, had stated firmly their own, quite different ideas.

'It breaks my heart, darling, but we don't baby-sit till we've met this. . .this new friend,' Lesley announced. 'After what Tom Evans did to you. . .'

And then she had had to cuddle Al, because how could you speak of him as a dirty trick, or even a misfortune? But she had meant it, and so had Piers. No introduction, no baby-sitting.

So item five had become item two. Patrick, dazzlingly handsome in white shirt and dark suit, duly presented himself for dinner at the Grove.

'Hm.' Claire's mother said afterwards. 'Well, I suppose it's all right. Don't make it a minute after eleven.'

This grudging consent cleared the way for the ask-out-to-dine item. Patrick took Claire to Simpson's in the Strand, where the superb, traditionally English meal could have been seaweed or sawdust for all she tasted of it. She was too worried about not touching him, keeping her high-heeled sandals strictly under her own chair while her hands and eyes busied themselves with the quickly forgotten food. In the outgoing and homegoing taxis they kept well away from each other, and he delivered her to the top of her own steps, not at eleven, but at ten-thirty.

'I don't like this,' Lesley Fletcher said, when her daughter came in alone at that early hour. 'It's not natural.'

She hadn't relented on that until two days later, when she let herself into the flat on one of her free afternoons. Claire was at her desk, Patrick in the armchair, firmly supporting Al's middle so that the little feet could practise standing. All were absorbed until Patrick saw Lesley and rose to his feet with his usual lithe grace, giving Al his long-awaited chance to grab Daphne's sparkly umbrellas. Claire and her mother took quite five minutes to sort man from baby and baby from mobile, and afterwards they were all friends.

'This Patrick of yours,' Lesley commented, 'he could be one of my side of the family, he's so fond of children.'

Item four, various outings with Al, worked out not at all various. They always took the same walk under the old trees of the common, with Al in the pushchair which had served all the Fletcher children. At weekends Matt came too, kicking his football to Patrick and demanding to be taught swimming.

Last Sunday, Patrick, elated with his success at items one-to-five, had added an item six. That was the day before he finally set off for the much-postponed drive to Scotland to visit his eagerly waiting parents.

'I've booked you a first-class sleeper for Friday,' he informed Claire, 'and Lesley says she'll have Al for the weekend.'

'But I'd meant to check a few things in the library. . .'

'You're coming to Erlington. It's your turn to be given the once-over.'

It seemed only fair, when you thought of it. Claire asked her father to bring her pearls home from the bank, brushed down her soberest tweeds, and was waved off from King's Cross by the entire home-based part of the family, with messages for her brother, Robert, if she should manage to get as far as Edinburgh.

Erlington House, when Patrick brought her to it yesterday morning turned out to be a much less grand place than it sounded. It wasn't even so very big—just a late-Victorian fantasy with absurd terracotta gargoyles and tiny round towers. The little lowlands town had long since grown out to meet it, and Dr Donovan had half of the ground floor for his surgery.

The older Donovans were as strictly respectable as she'd feared, but much kinder. It had been really good of them, for instance, to give her the chance of seeing Robert, and him a break from his medical studies, by inviting him for the weekend.

'I've no doubt that lad'll enjoy some home cooking,' Nan Donovan had responded to Claire's thanks. 'And the doctor will be glad enough to talk shop.'

She always called her husband 'the doctor' like that, perhaps because she saw the patients as much as he did. And Dr Donovan, a Patrick grown old, simply loved it. In his home he was king, carving Saturday's roast venison with pride, generous with praise for his wife's cooking.

'He doesn't often sit down for a proper meal,' Nan said later while she loaded the dishwasher. 'But he made a special point of this one, to celebrate Patrick's being sensible at last.'

'You think he is?' Claire asked eagerly.

'That new car. And, well——' the shrewed, dark blue eyes lengthened in a smile '—there's you.'

Here goes, Claire thought, and ran water into the washing-up bowl. 'I'll wash this other stuff, shall I?'

She started at once on the silver coffee-pot. It gave her something to do with her hands and her eyes, while she raised the difficult subject.

'You don't mind about my baby, then?'

'Not now I've met you.' Thus did devout, church-going Nan admit that she had once minded, perhaps a lot. 'You'll have paid for your mistake, over and over. Besides, a child. . .'

She closed the dishwasher, then looked, up, calm and brave. 'I wanted, oh, half a dozen. But Patrick was ten years coming, and there was never another.'

Claire felt herself flushing with familiar guilt, though in an entirely new form. Who would have thought that Patrick's mother would confess to being baby-starved? Would find, in being positive about her son's choice, the blessing that Claire had already proved able to bear children?

But I haven't, I haven't, she wanted to shout. Al's more your blood than mine—your grandson, maybe.

Instead, she washed the antler-handled carving-fork. 'He hasn't asked me to marry him, you know. Not. . .not really.'

But even that was a lie, in its way. He'd tried several times, not counting his first grudging approach to the idea in Tragana, or his headlong proposal two months ago, after Daphne had first brought them back together.

He'd been near the subject at regular intervals ever since. Mostly she'd managed to head him off, sometimes reminding him of his list, but mostly just dodging, with a lightness which had felt both trivial and false. She'd almost hated herself, and had certainly loathed this web of lies which wrapped her ever tighter.

'Run some water into the oven-tin, to soak,' Nan instructed, and gave her serene answer about her son. 'Not since he left for college, ten years ago, has he asked a girl up here to meet us.'

With infinite care, she lifted the inherited willow-pattern carving-plate, and handed it over. 'You can wash this, now.'

She was showing that she trusted me. Claire squirmed again on her comfortable ride through the rainy darkness. I just don't know how much longer I can bear it.

'The poor spring flowers,' she murmured as the wind buffetted the car. 'They'll be beaten to nothing but confetti. . .'

'So you're thinking of it, too.' Patrick slowed towards the thickening line of red tail-lights.

'Of. . .of what?' Fancy mentioning confetti, of all things!

He slowed further, closing up with the car in front. 'Well, here we are, nearly home.'

'It's been lovely.' She seized eagerly on the neutral topic. 'Breakfast in Scotland, lunch in Yorkshire——'

'And traffic jams on the M25 as usual. And for me, Whitehall next week.' He halted in the queue winding over the hill. 'I wonder what made me think the apple blossom would be out by now?'

'You can't win them all,' she joked desperately.

'Don't you *want* to marry me, Claire?'

She felt her hands clasping each other tight, and tried consciously to relax them. 'Why do you ask that?'

'Until now, I've made allowances. You've been hurt enough, goodness knows. If I ever get my hands on Tom Evans. . .'

The car behind hooted, and he had to edge up to the bumper in front. Claire shut her eyes, miserably aware that it wasn't just her hands but her whole body which was tight, drawn in, as small and secret as it could make itself.

'But surely I've proved by now I'm not like him?' Patrick kept his eyes on the dark outline of the car ahead. 'I can't believe some of the things I did before I met you.' He moved the car another yard or two forwards. 'That seems like a different person. You've changed me, Claire.'

It was all there in his voice, his beautiful, modulated voice with its Irish flexibility and its Scottish exactness. Its passion was mastered but fighting, as it had fought ever since he'd come back into her life.

And winning, she thought in a new wave of misery. He'd kept his resolve, changed himself, proved himself fit to marry and bring up a son. His own son, for goodness' sake. How could she go on trivialising that real achievement with stupid jokes, little pointless flurries, all the tricks she'd used till now to hold him away from her?

She couldn't. 'I know you have, Patrick, and I——' she winced as her nails dug into her palms '——I honour you for it.'

'You what?' That took his attention off the controls. 'What kind of an answer is that?'

'An honest one.'

'I don't want your damned honesty, or your damned honouring either. Or not only those.' He made an impatient gesture in the glaring on-off-on of the following car's flashing headlamps. 'Dammit, Claire. I want you as my wife. . .'

The car behind hooted, several times.

'To hell with this!'

He swung the wheel around and before she knew it they'd left the traffic at an exit which she hadn't even noticed. He drove without another word into a tiny side-turning, through a village, out the other side, and off the little road on to a grassy verge.

'Now.' His voice held a hint almost of menace. 'Are you going to blasted well marry me, or not?'

'Oh, my darling!' She collapsed in nervous laughter.

'What's so blasted funny?'

'Kew Gardens. Kent, and the apple orchards.' She really was amused, she realised, and it helped. 'And here we are, just off the M25, surrounded by traffic jams.'

'All right, so I don't get every damn thing right——' He broke off abruptly. 'Did I swear at you just now?'

'Several times. Specially during the proposals, if that's what they were.'

'Of course it's what they were, what do you damn well——' Another abrupt halt. 'I see what you mean.'

'I do love you, Patrick.'

'You do?' He sounded surprised. 'Even though I swear at you during the most romantic moment of a girl's life?'

'When I'm with you,' she discovered, equally surprised, 'every moment's romantic.'

And then it was all right. His arms were around her, his lips on hers where they should always have been. She accepted him hungrily because this was where he belonged, this was where they both belonged, together.

She should always have been able to do this. To run her fingers through his rosemary-scented hair, discover the groove at the nape of his neck, follow his collar to where she could slip her hand under the tweed jacket and explore the contours of the wide shoulders in their respectable Sunday shirt. And when his hand went to her knee, started to smooth its way up her patterned tights, that was all right too. . .

It was Patrick who drew back, breathing fast, his voice deep and hoarse. 'I'm not having this.'

'Wh-what?'

She could hardly force her mouth round even that little word. Her whole body was leaping, flowing, flaming, open with a longing which left mind and speech and reasoning somewhere far off, in a different world.

'I may have bodged the proposal, but that was only the. . .the other-people bit anyway.'

'The. . .other-people bit?' She tried to get herself together. 'I d-don't understand.'

'Families, contracts. . .' He left it at that. 'The real bit is you and me, joining till death do us part.' He sounded ever more in control. 'We're not doing that in any car.'

And then he was starting the engine, easing them off the verge and on to the little road between the dark hedges.

Claire struggled with her disappoinment. How could he do this to her? It had all become to simple. No more thinking, no more worrying what to say, what to tell and how, everything just happening the way it had to and somehow resolving itself.

The hedges gave way to houses, streets, a small town with a school, a park, a church, two pubs. Patrick eased the car to a halt in front of the Swan, and silenced the engine and wipers.

Claire sat quietly, soothed by the peaceful sounds of small-town life. A car droned in the distance, a gutter plashed, a dog pattered by with its raincoated owner, and the trees overhead released great petal-laden drops on to the windscreen before her eyes.

'I. . . I like it here,' Patrick began, unusually hesitant for him. 'Do you?'

She understood at once. 'I do, Patrick. I do.'

Her heart knocked so loudly that she was surprised he couldn't hear it. But it felt so right now. Her parents weren't expecting her to pick up Al until midday tomorrow—her mother was taking a free morning, the better to enjoy having her grandson to herself. She'd told Claire not to hurry, but to have a good lie-in after the long, late journey from Scotland.

And here was Patrick, taking her left hand and kissing the third finger. Here were his lips, his rosemary-scented hair, his length and breadth, his peaks and ridges and hollows. . .

'I do,' she affirmed once more.

Once out of the car, she very much liked the look of the Swan. It had clearly been the town's original coaching-inn, with a wide archway and cobbled yard and low outbuildings which must once have been stables. Next to the archway, a warm-lit, pillared entrance was near enough to step into and shelter from the rain. Under its roof, bay trees flanked a gold-lettered glass case with a gold swan on top of it and a lavish menu within.

She smiled to see Patrick coming towards her from his side of the car. The rain wasn't worrying him; he almost seemed to shoulder it aside like a lion treading through long grass.

'That's it.' She pointed beyond him. 'That's our place.'

The pub across the street was equally old, but simpler. Its white-plastered façade had little ornamentation; only a notice in one of its sash-windows offering 'Bed and Breakfast—Vacancies'. The sign which had caught her eye was painted over the doorway along with a realistic tawny image of its kingly namesake.

'The Lion?' He kissed her cheek, his arm possessive at her waist. 'Whatever you say, my darling.'

'It's meant,' she breathed. 'We're joining our lives under the sign of the Lion.'

Only to herself did she add, It shows it'll be all right.

It helped her during the business of parking the car, bringing out the luggage, enquiring in the bar. They hadn't eaten yet, but when the Lion's muscular, grey-haired proprietor offered supper, both shook their heads at once. Another good omen, Claire decided as the man departed and left them in their cosy room.

She was vaguely aware of roses everywhere. Yes, the

wallpaper and counterpane and curtains all had the same rosebud pattern, and the carpet was rose-wreathed.

'S-somebody's furnished this with love,' she offered, trying to control her quavery voice.

'They must have known we were coming.'

He put a hand out as if to cup her chin, but didn't touch her. Instead the hand turned, traced in the air the outline of her long neck, and stayed parallel with the base of her throat.

'I've dreamed about this.'

'S-so have I.' But for all that, she broke away.

She knew that she was flurrying again, but she couldn't help it. She had to switch on the rose-shaded bedside-lamp, switch off the top light, feel the temperature of the radiator.

'This is hot already——'

'So am I, my darling.' This time he took a firm grip, one hand on her fussing wrist, the other on her waist, turning her towards him and refusing to let her go. 'So am I.'

It came out muffled, his lips against the tender inner side of the wrist which he had captured. They slid to the centre of her palm and she stood motionless, loving him.

He raised his head, and folded her fingers over her palm where his lips had touched. While she looked down at her own short, unpainted nails, all in a row to hold in his kiss, he loosened her hair, and used his own hands to comb the heavy, barely waving length of it down over her shoulders.

Then he took her mouth.

At once their bodies strained together through the muffling layers of winter clothing. His hand found its way under her sweater, down her spine and over her waist and up to one eager, lace-covered breast.

Now she, too, was aflame, impatient with all the different fabrics that held them apart. She must be rid of them, meet him free and untrammelled, join him in the special, marvellous way that men and women could join, should join, had always been meant to join.

She broke away, and switched off the bedside-light. In the street-light which filtered white through the rosebud curtains, she found her way to the other side of the bed and shed clothes with her back to him.

'Not like that,' he pleaded. 'I want to see you.'

But she had a plea of her own. 'Hurry, Patrick, do hurry. *I* want to *be* with you, close.'

And then they were close, with cool sheets wrapping them in their own private world. Under those sheets he was all heat; hot arms drawing her to hot, rough chest; hot, hard belly and thighs; and here, that other flame she longed for yet feared even as she pressed to it.

'Not so fast, my darling.' He pushed her back on to the mattress, and rose above her. 'We've a whole lifetime for this.'

Was that why she shivered with her hair so heavy about her and his maleness so hot against her? Could it be this vision which was chilling her? Of a whole different life, new and enormous, stretching away further than you could see in every direction?

One of his hands smoothed her thigh, her hip, her waist, and the shivering stopped. She felt his tongue at the base of her throat, then on the upper slopes of her breasts. It lingered there so long that she made a small, impatient noise. His only response was to draw back, deliberately tormenting.

'You taste of roses.'

She drew a long, trembling breath, and slowed down as he had told her she must. 'They're. . .they're flowering.'

'I know.'

But still he held away from the flowers. Instead, he covered them with the length of her hair, and laughed as its glossy, dark strands dropped away, pushed away it seemed by the urgent stirrings beneath.

She laughed, too, because now she could play the game with him. Here was his wide, strong shoulder, so different from her own, and here his hard chest, covered with this strange, wiry softness of hair. And these were his ribs, and here they stopped, and here was the darling little whorl of his navel. And here, here, here. . .

A little hissing noise, his breath sharply drawn in through his teeth, and he had her wrist again. He pinned it to the pillow by her head, and kissed her hard on the mouth.

'All right, my darling. You win.'

And then came a pleasure such as she had never known. But yes, she had known it once before, this leaping flame as his mouth found her breasts. She had known it in Tragana, only then it had been bad, and now it was good. Now she could run her fingers through his hair, play them over his body, rejoice in the firmness of his flesh as he rejoiced in hers, let the Tragana flame engulf her and open her to pleasure and a great beginning and a new life.

Only, it hurt. It hurt so much that she had to whimper aloud, and that made something happen to him. She didn't understand what, only that the joy had gone, the inner brightness dimmed. Though their bodies still intertwined, they weren't together any more.

But even that didn't last much longer. Somehow he got away from her, and sat up, and switched on the bedside-light.

'Did you——' He broke off, sad and puzzled. 'Did you have such a very bad time with Al? Is that what's done this to you?'

She wanted to cry. She *was* crying, her eyes wet and her voice clogged in her throat so that she couldn't speak, only turn from him and curl herself together.

'Don't do that, my darling, I can't bear it.'

And he forcibly pulled her round to him, straightening her stiff, resisting limbs so that her body was once more open to him. But it wasn't her body he wanted now, she knew that. It was her mind, her heart, the truth about herself.

'We're still us.' His voice came out gravelly with stemmed passion, but he wasn't angry with her; not yet. 'Whatever this is, we can get it together. We'll see specialists. . .'

That brought on the crying in good earnest. The loud sobs were a kind of relief, but only until she felt his arms around her, his shoulder under her wet cheek.

Those should have been a comfort, but the rest of her was too close to him. Close enough to send to her stupefied, selfish mind the message of a healthy male unsatisfied. And her mind didn't care; it just went on pushing out tears, shaking down sobs, letting him stroke her back exactly the way she stroked Al's, letting him murmur these meaningless words of comfort which only made her hate herself more.

Presently she sat up. 'I need a hanky.'

'That's better.' Still lying down, he reached for his scattered pile of clothes, brought up his jacket by its tail, and searched it unmercifully. 'Have mine.'

'This is a hanky?' She shook open its zebra-stripes. 'I thought you must be carrying a little tent around in your pocket.'

But she couldn't cheer herself up.

'Haven't you a proper one?' Her own question rang thin and crotchety in her ears. 'I can't blow my nose on this.'

'Yes, you can.' He dropped the jacket on to the floor, and lay back on the pillow. 'I do myself, all the time.'

'Liar. I've never seen you blow your nose *once*, on this

or anything——' She stopped. 'How did we get to blowing noses?'

'I think it's something to do with "in sickness and in health".' He turned on his side to kiss her arm. '"For better or for worse."' He pushed her hair from her breasts, and darted his tongue at one gathered crest like a boy at a lollipop. 'These are for better——'

'Don't.' She winced away.

'It's all right, my darling, it's all right.' He, too, sat up, splendid torso exposed. 'We won't do a thing you don't want.'

'That's not it at all.' She remembered the urgent male need, now blessedly hidden beneath the rosebud counterpane. 'I *do* want it. . .want *you*, I mean. . . Not quite yet, perhaps, but. . .' Her anger with herself suddenly exploded. '*Hell*!'

In the silence that followed, rain blew against the window. It must have come on harder; she could hear it pattering on the leaves outside, and splashing in the gutters.

'This is being quite a day,' Patrick said at last. 'I curse when I'm proposing, you curse when we're. . .whatever this is.'

'It's me I'm cursing.' She pulled the counterpane up as far as it would go under her arms.

'You needn't.' He reached for her hand. 'It'll come right.'

'It won't. Or not till I've told you——'

She broke off, and swallowed hard. This was decision-time with a vengeance, forced on her by her own cowardly refusal to take any of the better chances which she'd passed over.

'Patrick,' she began carefully, 'I didn't think it was going to be so. . .' What a mess she was making of this. 'You're the first. . . I mean. . . No, that's it.' She realised that she had stumbled on a way of saying it. 'You were the first.'

He turned to stare at her. She kept her head bowed, letting her hair hide most of her face.

'And Al?' he asked at last.

She drew a deep breath, and slumped back miserably on her pillow. 'You'd better hear it all.'

And she told it, baldly, in as few words as possible.

'So you see,' she finished to his frowning, intent silence, 'he could be more yours than mine. Though I couldn't love him any more than I do——'

She had to break off; her throat was clogging again. And still he didn't speak, didn't move, didn't try to comfort her or give any sign that he either liked or hated what she'd done.

Then, when he seemed to have kept her waiting forever, he lay back among the pillows. 'I was going to find Tom Evans some day, and beat him to a pulp.'

'Were you?' Inquisitiveness revived her a little. 'You never told me.'

'I couldn't talk about him, I hated him so much.' He closed his eyes and shook his head, completely foxed. 'That's a lot of good hate wasted.'

'All hate's best wasted.'

He reacted at once to her sharp tone, propping himself up on one elbow. 'You've been stringing me along, Claire Fletcher-that-was-to-be-Donovan.'

'Was?' She picked up the dreaded word with the quickness of her pain and confusion.

'Is, I suppose,' he amended. But he didn't touch her. 'I feel like I never knew you at all.'

'Does it. . .' She tried to keep the pleading note from her voice. 'Does it make so very much difference?' But of course it did. How could she ask anything so silly? She must cover the question with another. 'What are you going to do?'

'I don't know.' The dark blue eyes grew distant and thoughtful. 'Last June, before I met you, I'd have been out of here this minute, looking for Donna. Now, though——'

'You needn't stay for my sake,' she snapped, pride sour in her mouth. 'You don't owe me anything.'

'If you think that, then you've missed the whole point of these last two months.'

'Oh, for heaven's sake!'

She flung back the sheets, and rushed for her weekend-case. Soon she was swathed, neck, wrist and ankle, in the navy, cotton pyjamas which she had chosen to keep her warm when north of the Border.

Clothed and nearer her right mind, she found Patrick at the same task. He stood by his case in damson poplin trousers, shrugging on a stylish top that came to his knees.

'Talk about the male bird wearing the plumage.' She made to sit on the bed, and jumped up from it as if electrocuted.

He gave her a distracted frown. 'Now what?'

'We've got to sleep together.'

'And sleep is what we'll do. Or what I'll do.' He sank to his side of the bed, and flung out his arms in a great, stretching yawn. 'I told you, I've changed. Or I'm getting older.'

'You expect us to share this bed?' She could hardly believe it. 'After all this?'

'All what? I don't know what you've done,' he added, not waiting for her answer. 'I don't know what I've done.' He slid under the covers and settled into his side of the bed. 'I don't know who you are any more, I'm not sure about me, and that's before I start thinking about——'

His calm almost broke up then, but he recovered it in time.

'About Al,' he finished. 'But there's one thing I do know. This bed's comfortable, and we're going to get a night's rest in it.' He pulled back the covers on her side. 'Come on.'

Slowly, reluctantly, unable to disobey him, she edged on to the mattress. It *is* comfortable, she realised, lying down.

'One of the things I've learned these last months——' he put out the light and drew her into his arms '——is to think a problem through. Plan it out. Walk round it. In short, to sleep on it.'

'Oh, dear.' About to relax close to him, she started away from his stirring maleness. 'How can I do this to you. . .?'

'You're not doing anything but being Claire.' He stroked her neck. 'You never did anything but that.'

'But how can you sleep?

'That's *my* problem.' And he turned on his back and edged a little away, so perhaps that was how he dealt with it. 'Sleep, little archer. Sleep.'

And presently, his regular breathing showed that he was doing exactly that. Claire wanted to stay away from him, but an animal warmth stole out of his body, drawing her to nestle to its slow-breathing, sleeping length. And the rosebud curtains were so pretty in the street-light, and the rain drummed so agreeably on the window, and the church clock chimed so sweetly across the rooftops; one, two, three, four, five, six, seven. . ,

It was morning.

CHAPTER EIGHT

'We've got to eat something,' Claire insisted, more for herself than for Patrick. 'We can't face Monday morning on an empty stomach.'

Before last night, he would have lovingly called her 'Bossy-boots'. Now, he only gave her an absent-minded glance before turning to the shy, bright-eyed landlady of the Lion.

'Coffee and toast'll be fine, thanks.'

They were at a damask-spread window-table, in a small dining-room overlooking the garden. The toast arrived in a silver rack covered by a damask napkin and the coffee in a silver pot on a silver chafing dish, and each was the best of its kind.

'Who'd have thought it would be so sumptuous,' Claire ventured nervously, 'in this little place?'

'Eh? Oh.' He brought his attention to her with an obvious effort. 'I think she's making a fuss for the young lovers.'

'If only she knew.'

But he'd gone again, staring at that eastern sky, and she knew exactly why because she felt it, too. Under that wide sky flushed with sunrise, though lawn and daffodils sparkled with last night's rain, the green view faded to a mere ghostly overlay. Through it, the daylight slowly brightened the fast-flowing Danube, and the peach-coloured outer walls of her cell soaked up the renewed heat of a southern day.

'We'd better eat.' Patrick offered her the two cut-glass bowls on their silver, lion-handled tray. 'I wish this was caviare, don't you?'

She took a pale corner of butter and a dark runnel of marmalade. 'You're not really wishing that.'

'Aren't I?' He helped himself liberally, and sampled the marmalade. 'Well, maybe not. This is good.'

'But not caviare.'

'Caviare, marmalade, they're two such different things.' He finished his toast and reached for more. 'I'm hungrier than I thought. I'd forgotten we didn't have supper last night.'

Remembering what they had instead, she bit her lip, and stared down at her own untouched toast.

The minute that she'd woken up half an hour ago, she'd hurried along the corridor to the bathroom. She'd returned showered and dressed, to find Patrick shaved and dressing-gowned and collecting his clothes for the same mission. They'd packed self-consciously, making way for each other like strangers and discussing the rest of their journey in flat, neutral tones.

And in another minute or two we'll be on our way. And we can't talk on the M25, not properly, her confused brain nagged. It has to be here, or maybe never.

The coffee at least was welcome, as fresh as its aroma promised. It stirred her sluggish mind to a new whirl of questions, so she asked one of them before the enormity of it could frighten her.

'Do you mind my being marmalade instead of caviare?'

As usual, he understood her at once. However, he didn't answer in her own terms as he'd always done until now, but chose instead to translate her words into ordinary, prosaic facts.

'You mean, do I mind your being a virgin, not a mother.'

She looked round anxiously; she couldn't help it. But it was all right, they were completely alone.

'Let's face it, I'm miffed.' He finished his coffee, and

pushed the cup across for more. 'Part of me says you could have trusted me, back there in Tragana.'

'If you think that,' she flared, 'you've a short memory.'

'I haven't.' His reflective tone didn't change. 'But all the same. . . And then there's Tom Evans. Do I get more coffee?'

She mumbled an apology, and refilled his cup.

'Backpacking,' he went on as he sipped it. 'Tasmania. It's been such a complicated lie.'

And she, a truth-loving Sagittarius, had spun its every detail. The points of sunlight on breakfast silver went suddenly blurry and she had to turn her head, fiddling in her bag for a handkerchief. The one she brought out was enormous and zebra-striped, which somehow made things worse.

She hid in it and pretended to be sneezing. 'I'll g-get this back to you when I've washed it.'

'No need. I've plenty more.'

Was that just his Leo grandeur refusing to be bothered with details? Or was he making sure that she'd have no excuse to seek him out, once he'd got rid of her?

But he can't get rid of me, she thought, lost in the old, bewildering maze. I have his son. If Al is his son.

'But if Al's my son, then I'm the original reason you had to tell all those lies. Funny, that.' He took more toast, staring out at the glittering garden. 'It's the same——' the dark blue eyes sought hers '—the same passion, whatever comes of it. But if there's a baby, it changes everything.'

'Well, babies do.' She remembered Al's urgent crying in the frightening silence of Tragana, how his basic needs had kept her busy, and the comfort of holding him had kept her sane. 'He. . .he changed everything for me, too.'

'Didn't he just?' Patrick spread his toast. 'I'll have to make sure you finish that thesis. It's the least I can do.'

She stared at him in disbelief. 'That isn't what I. . . You surely don't think. . .'

'The lying, the worry, the work—it's all cost you dear.' He emptied his cup. 'This coffee's good.'

How could he sit there eating and drinking, at a time like this? She gave him the last of the coffee, blew out the candle in the chafing dish, and watched the wax-scented thread of smoke wreathe away from the black, bereaved wick.

He emptied the cup quickly. 'Where was I?'

And he prepared to go on with his wretched, calm discussion, as if none of this was anything to do with him. 'Ah, yes. If you go back far enough, the finger points straight at me.' He put the cup quietly in its saucer. 'It's all my fault—but we can't talk like that, can we?'

She pushed away her plate, giving up any hope of eating. So Patrick was still Patrick after all, inconstant as ever under his shallow two-month reform. What could she say now, what could she do, to convince him that he had to be serious about this?

'Why can't we talk about it?' she demanded. 'It's not something to be run away from.'

He looked up, frowning. Then he put down his knife, gripped the table, and leaned towards her.

'Have you ever known me run away from anything? Have you?'

'This is no time for your stinking Leo pride,' she raged. 'People have endless ways of dodging their problems——'

'And I despise all of them.'

'There you go, master of the known universe.' What a relief to criticise him, to forget the fear and worry of recent weeks and just give him his character in so many words. 'Has it ever occurred to you that there might be things you don't understand?'

The deep blue eyes narrowed. 'Last night, for instance?'

'Exactly. Last night you found out how I'd cleared up your mess for you, back there in Tragana——'

She stopped herself, horrified. To speak of Al as a *mess*! Nothing could justify her even thinking of him like that; it made her not fit to be his mother.

'I see you've got there at last.' His words hit like icicles, freezing and stabbing. 'As I was saying when you started throwing punches, we can't talk about Al as a *fault*.' The dark eyes held hers in cold triumph. 'Let alone as a *mess*.'

'I. . . I didn't mean that. I didn't know what I was——'

'He's a human being, with rights.'

'For heaven's sake!' She bent to cram the striped hanky in her bag. 'Do you think I need a lecture on that?'

'How do I know what you need?' The generous mouth tightened in growing impatience. 'You've turned into somebody quite different from the woman I took you for.'

'I haven't.' She flung her napkin on her plate. 'And I don't have to be told what's best for my own. . .'

She trailed off, staring down at her empty cup. In the ever more painful silence, sparrows bickered round the bird-bath in the garden. Milk-bottles rattled, a car engine started up, the church clock chimed nine.

'That's it, isn't it? However much you want him to be, he isn't. . .who you said.' Patrick's voice was sober, his anger already forgotten. 'And who he really is——' He broke off to stare at her, deep in his own thoughts. 'That,' he finished at last, 'is what has to be settled. Fast.'

She gripped her hands fiercely together, under the table where he couldn't see them. She must follow his example, stay calm, never, ever do what her soul demanded. Not on any account must she rise up and scream in his face that Al was hers, and nothing and nobody was going to take him away from her.

He showed no awareness of her battle for self-control; not the flicker of an eyelid. He was too busy eating his wretched toast, and then rising before he'd even finished it.

'I must get to the airport.'

'The what?' Please, please let her have heard wrong.

'As soon as I've dropped you off at home——' he crumpled his own napkin by his plate, and pushed away the heavy dining-chair '—I must go to Vienna.'

How could he? And if he had to do it, surely he could at least keep it to himself until he was out of her sight? Surely he could do that little thing, not to hurt her any worse than she was being hurt already?

But clearly, none of that occurred to him. He paid the bill and charmed the landlady, then loaded the bags into the car with such haste that he might have been. . . He might have been preparing to meet the woman he loved.

On the motorway, she had nothing to do but recognise it. The glittery morning was a weariness to her eyes, but when she closed them she saw only Patrick, alert and revived as he'd been when he'd risen from that old-fashioned dining-chair, pushed it aside, and crumpled his napkin by his plate.

Left them because he didn't need them any more. The humble, useful objects had served their purpose, and now he was off to more important things. Off to find his old love, his real love, the real mother of his child.

Listen to him now, humming at the wheel in that deep, velvety voice. The humming became words, so soft that she wouldn't have heard them over the road noises if she hadn't already known them.

'He's my guy,
I don't care what he does,
For he's my guy,
I guess he always was. . .'

He had to stop there, to read the signs at a junction.

He means, She's my gal, Claire thought bitterly. But I don't suppose he even knows he's saying it.

To make matters worse, the M25 had another blockage this morning. By the time he carried her bag into her flat they were almost at her deadline—the time she had agreed to meet her mother in the basement-kitchen of the main house.

'Are you coming to see your. . .my. . .' Claire tried again. 'Are you coming to say hello to Al?'

'No, thanks, love.' He bent to her cheek, and would have pecked it if she hadn't dodged away.

'Don't do that,' she spat at him, unable to bear such a casual display of affection.

He straightened, frowned, and glanced at his watch. 'Spare me the temperament just now, love. . .'

'And don't call me "love", either. It doesn't mean a thing.'

He didn't answer her in words. However, his deep sigh and his air of self-control were worse than if he'd snapped at her. And when he did speak it was of something quite different, as if to distract a fractious child.

'I'd have offered to bring the cot back from the main house,' he murmured soothingly, 'but I see it's here already.'

She glanced at the cot, crowded into its usual place under the sparkly umbrellas. How much longer would it be there? She turned her head away, from it and from him, and made herself very busy unzipping her bag.

'I expect your father, or David, or Matt, must have

brought it up,' he offered, still in that infuriating, reasoning style of a responsible grown-up with a five-year-old.

At least the aggravation held back her tears so that she could face him. 'Will you please go?'

'And leave you like this?'

'Just *go*.' She almost stamped like the child he was taking her for.

He frowned. 'What's got into you? You know we both need this——'

'I know *what*?' She could hardly believe her ears. 'What did I ever see in you, Patrick Donovan?'

'Oh, for——' He broke off, and cast his eyes to heaven. Then, having shown how silly she was being, and how patient he was to put up with her, he continued.

'I'm not going to hang about here and waste time arguing with you. But before I go——' he took a step forward, and towered over her '——I'm going to show you what you see in me.'

And he did, and she couldn't stop him. At first, because he pinned her hands to her back, and trapped her between himself and the cot. Then because the only thing she wanted was to stay here in the circle of his arms, his hard mouth on her, his hard body her governor and shield, hers and Al's against the world.

'See?' He drew away from her, panting. 'There's more, but that'll do to be going on with.'

'It won't.'

But she wasn't angry now. Too much of her strength had drained away, leaving nothing but grey resignation. She squeezed round him to the door, and opened it wide.

'I'm glad you're going.'

'Are you?' He lingered, perplexed and suspicious. 'You're not acting glad.'

'I am, though.'

And she would be, quite soon. As soon as her wretched

body had ceased its silent uproar. As soon as her blind, unruly heart had stopped jumping with the need to keep him here. As soon as her mind was in control, then she'd know how much better she'd be without this man who used women and left them like old-fashioned chairs, like cumpled napkins.

'Poor Donna Cortesi,' she murmured, almost to herself. 'She doesn't know what she's got coming to her.'

But that was worse than useless, much worse. Whatever Donna Cortesi had to suffer in the future, whatever she had suffered in the past, she was to have her son back. She would take Al and Patrick, and leave nothing here but a double emptiness. . .

Not double, she frantically contradicted herself, not double.

Because how could Patrick be any loss? Look at him now, springing cat-like on the name of his last love.

'I told you, Donna won't ever be poor. But you're right——' the dark blue eyes blazed '——she certainly doesn't know what she's got coming.'

And he was gone. Claire shut the door at once, but she heard him whistling as he clattered down the outside steps. Whistling! She went to the window, cursing herself for being a fool yet unable to quell her useless longing. She had to open the window as she'd opened it two months ago, had to see him down there in the street as she'd seen him then, on that winter day when all the world had burst into blossom.

There he was on the pavement, waving to her, jingling his car keys, still whistling.

He never really loved me, she thought. And soon, I'll know I never loved him, either. As for that damn song. . .

'Hello, Patrick.' It was her mother, leaning out of the sash-window of the drawing-room. 'I was beginning to wonder——' She stopped, so as not to tell the street what she'd been wondering. 'How was Scotland?'

'Magnificent as ever.' He unlocked his car. 'And your daughter was a huge success with my parents.'

How could he say such things? Claire felt her eyes sting at his heartless good humour, and summoned all her fiery, Sagittarian temper to drive back the tears.

He's not worth it, she told herself. He was never the man for you, Claire Fletcher. Never, never, never.

But all that produced was more of the wretched song he'd put on her. 'Nobody knows, better than I,' it sang back at her, 'that he's my guy.'

'I suppose you've made yourself late for something?' Lesley was asking with less than her usual indulgence.

'Not late, exactly.' Even as he turned his great Leo head up to the window, he was preparing to lower himself into his driving seat. 'But yes, it's urgent. Ask Claire, she'll explain.'

'As if I ever could——'

Claire stopped, but by then it was too late. Two pairs of eyes were fixed on her, and her mother's were reading all too clearly the droop of her shoulders, the curve of her neck, the disheartened dip of her head.

She lifted it. 'Right, Patrick. I'll be hearing from you.'

'You will.' He blew her a kiss, and vanished under the glaring, polished roof of his car.

· I won't cry, Claire told herself. I won't. I won't.

And she didn't. Instead she watched the car nose away under trees harsh with spring sunlight, past great lumps of other cars, and slide roaring into the high street like a sinner into Hell.

'Claire?' Lesley's voice sharpened from her own window. 'You didn't eat any breakfast.'

'Didn't I?' Claire tried to remember if she had or not.

'You're always like this when you don't eat,' Lesley asserted with maternal confidence. 'Come in here at once, and have lunch.'

Which made it easier, in a way. So did Al, though

when Claire went down to the big basement-kitchen she wasn't sure how she could bear even to see him again. But, after all, he was still hers in every sense that mattered; she knew that the minute he crowed and held out his arms from his high-chair.

And Lesley asked no awkward questions, though she would plainly have liked to. 'Really, darling, you might have phoned.'

'But you're not expecting me for another——' Claire glanced at her watch '—another ten minutes.'

'You were supposed to be home last night. The Donovans said you set off in good time.'

'You rang them?'

'Of course we did, when your father took the cot back and found you still weren't home,' Lesley defended herself. 'It's a long way; you could have had an accident.'

She chewed the inside of her lower lip, grey eyes examining her daughter, missing nothing. Then, on an air of decision, she took charge of Al in a way that brooked no refusal, and gestured down at the big table where she had set one place.

'Eat, child.'

The flan was still warm, and only a quarter gone. It was the kind with cottage cheese and spinach beaten into the eggs instead of bacon and onion. None of the men in the family liked it, but Claire did.

How can I be hungry, she wondered, at a time like this?

But she was. The flan seemed to melt away. While she ate, her mother moved about the kitchen with Al on one arm, preparing the briefcase which she would presently take to afternoon classes, and fending off Al's attempts to sabotage it. Not until the plates were empty, their entire contents on their way to her daughter's empty stomach, did she make the great announcement.

'The tooth's through.'

'It is?'

Claire shot to her feet, as her mother had known she would, and grabbed her son. Yes, there it was, a little white sharpness in the coral-pink gum.

'Glug,' Al objected.

'Who's a clever darling?' Claire rested her cheek on his feathery, dark hair. 'Who can give his din-dins a good bite now?'

Lesley opened her mouth, and closed it again on her often-repeated arguments against baby-talk. Instead she smiled, content that her cheer-up recipe had worked, then paused on a new worry.

'Er—your father and I have this centenary dinner tonight.'

Claire nodded. She'd helped choose the dress.

'We won't be home till the small hours.'

Lesley's loving thoughts were plain. Would her daughter be miserable again, back in her lonely flat with nobody to distract her and nobody to talk to about this row or whatever it was?

But Claire had made her resolve on that one. Until these questions hanging over Al were answered, her parents must know nothing of them. And if the answers were the worst possible. . .

But no, she couldn't think about that. 'I'll be all right.'

Still Lesley hovered. 'Sure?'

'Honest. I'm much better now.'

At the time, that was almost true. With food inside her she felt, if not better, at least stronger. She could take Al up to the drawing-room and let him explore the carpet, well cleared of dangerous objects like the banished glass coffee-table, then wrap him snug and wheel him to the sunny common, without thinking that this might be the last time that she ever did such things.

Or, at least, without thinking of it too often. She stayed out much, much longer than usual, hungrily storing up memories. This mittened flourish Al made towards a red double-decker bus, this comic surprise at the cheeky aproach of a robin, this friendly interest in a staggering toddler whose nurse walked alongside to chat—memories of these, memories of Al, might soon be all she had left.

We could run away, she thought in a moment of mad defiance. But the idea was ludicrous. Run away from Patrick, who was most likely Al's father? Run away from her own loving parents, and all the help they had given her?

Returning to her flat brought her almost to the edge. Maybe it was the sight of her bag waiting to be unpacked on the bed, or maybe it was Al himself, crabby with fatigue as she put him through his evening routine.

'Mummy should have brought you home much sooner, shouldn't she, muffin?' she soothed as she changed and fed him. 'No nap this afternoon, no wonder you're so tired.'

At any rate he'd worked up an appetite, and, when he'd satisfied it, was more willing than usual to settle for the night. And only when he was fully asleep, his battered teddy beside him on the pillow and the sparkly umbrellas slowly twirling above his head, only then did Claire lie face-down on her own narrow bed and let her feelings rip.

After being held in so hard, they ripped with a vengeance. She did manage not to wail too loud, and to muffle her sobs in the pillow, but they seemed to last an eternity. Every time she thought she could get up and drag herself to her little bathroom to splash cold water on her burning eyes, another lot would shake right through her—and another, and another. Only exhaustion finally stemmed them, and, even then, more would have got through if the phone hadn't rung.

Her first impulse was to ignore it, her next, that it

might be Patrick. But he couldn't possibly have made Vienna and back in—she looked at her watch—in seven hours. And anyway, she never wanted to speak to him again. So why did her heart start this wretched, wild dance at the very idea?

'Because he'll have news for you, fool.' She reached for the receiver. 'He hasn't had time to get back, but he could easily have been there long enough to. . .'

No, she didn't want to know what he'd had long enough to do. Not to think about it, she lifted the phone.

'At last.' Vienna must be a noisy place; he was having to shout to hear himself. 'Seven always was my lucky number.'

'S-seven?' She put her hand over the mouthpiece to conceal the choked, left-over sob that escaped her throat.

'I've already tried to ring you six times.'

'S-six?' she echoed, unbelieving.

'Did you know,' he teased, 'that you can say other things into a phone besides numbers? Try it.'

How could he be so light-hearted, so light-minded, at such a time? A new wave of anger with him pushed back her tears and jolted her mind nearer to working order.

'I'm surprised you could make that many calls, what with. . .with meeting Donna and all.'

'I haven't, and anyway, I'd always——' A new roar shattered the background, and he gave up the struggle to convey whatever it was. 'How's our boy?'

Our boy. His and Donna's. She looked down at Al, who was flushed and tranquil and breathing evenly, and pushed away yet again the thought of how little time she might have left with him.

'He is yours, then?'

Merely to ask it made her heart leap against her ribs as if it were trying to get out. And why had her head gone floating away from the rest of her? And what was he saying? How could he possibly *not know yet*?

, 'Hasn't she told you?' Claire tried to imagine the events that might have prevented it. 'Has she a concert? Is she away from home? Couldn't you see her——'

'Shut up a minute,' he ordered against the echoing hubbub. 'She says she's got to see the boy. . .'

'So he's hers.' A final, wan hope crumbled to dust. 'You'll be bringing her back with you from Vienna, then?'

'Will you listen? I'm not in Vienna, I'm at *London Airport*.'

'And that's as far as you've got? In seven hours?'

'There's her flight being called.' He must mean the noise now recognisable as a loudspeaker. 'It shows what you've done to me, Claire Fletcher; I clean forgot the phone had been invented.'

'You mean,' she struggled to understand, 'you just stayed in London, and rang her?'

'Brilliant, isn't it?'

'But how did you know her number?'

'Directory Enquiries. Her Count Whatsisname's given her a business line of her own, for when the call comes.'

'The call?' Claire repeated, bewildered. 'But did she know you were going to ring?'

'Not me, gump! The idea is——' his exaggerated patience could be heard through all the racket '—when the Scala, or the Met, need a Queen of the Night, they'll have no trouble reaching her.'

'So you just talked to her on the phone?' Claire's idiot brain at last began to hoist it in. 'You never went anywhere?'

'I went to the nearest coin box, then to my flat, where I tried to ring you four times——'

'But you knew I was at the main house.'

'Oddly enough, I did think of that. It was permanently engaged.'

'That's funny. There must be something wrong with——'

'Then I came out to the airport,' he continued on a martyred note, as if she ought to have got all this by now. 'Stopping off twice on the way to try and reach you.'

'Maybe that was when I was on the common.'

'Fancy,' he exclaimed sarcastically. 'Are you back from there now?'

'There's no need to——'

'I mean, are you with me this far?'

'I. . . I think so.'

She fought off her desire to make the angry retort that he could have explained himself more clearly. One of them at least had to stick to the point.

'You called Donna Cortesi——' she pronounced the name with an effort '——and told her you knew where her. . .her son was. And she believed you?'

'When I told her about Tragana, yes.'

'You told her that.' Why did it seem such a betrayal?

'The description of you convinced her. She knows all about you. She used to—er—watch you.' The eerie idea must have impressed even his heedless mind. 'From a window. When you walked in the garden.'

'Was that how she came to rig up the baby-alarm? The one in the corridor, outside my cell,' she added, impatient in her turn at his slowness. 'The one that helped me find him.'

'We hadn't time to go into details.'

'I suppose not.' The picture was beginning to form. 'The minute she heard about Al, she'd want to see him.'

'As a matter of fact, yes.' Why did he sound so surprised? 'She couldn't get me off the line fast enough to book her flight.'

It was no more than Claire had expected; exactly

what she herself would have done. 'She must have rung again, though, to tell you when to meet her.'

'Got it. And here I am, a taxi service at the ready.'

'You're bringing her here by taxi?' Claire asked, puzzled once more. 'But didn't you take your own car?'

'I only meant. . . Skip it.' He gave up the effort to explain what he only meant. 'Yes, I've got my car here. We'll be with you as quick as we can make it.'

'We,' she repeated, trying to get used to that word which, because it meant him and Al and another woman, was going to alter her whole life.

'Hello,' his voice barked from the earpiece. 'Are you still there? Did you hear?'

'I heard.' Her own voice sounded curiously cold and dead in her ears.

'God knows how long it'll take us—rush-hour traffic won't be over yet. You'll wait?'

'I'm not going anywhere.' Not anywhere that mattered, not ever again.

'Are you all right? Look, Claire, whatever comes of this——' He broke off as the pips sounded. 'That's it. The end of my phonecard. For heaven's sake don't. . .' He gave up. 'Hell and damnation, I''ll be with you as quick as——'

And that was it. Nothing but an empty line, an empty life.

Or not quite empty, not yet. Al was still here, waking and holding out his arms to be cuddled. Dropping his battered blue teddy, and smiling like an angel when it knocked over the vase of anemones which Lesley had put on the window-sill to welcome their return. And, at last, resting in his cot again with teddy safe by him, blinking up at his umbrellas and finally losing his regular battle against sleep.

Would Donna Cortesi understand this habit he had of waking for one last fling before he gave in? Would she know how to persuade him to let his hair be washed? Would she make sure that he didn't kick his blankets off, and feed him the mashed banana he loved, and coax into him the carrots which he was less keen about?

Because if she doesn't, thought Claire, she can't have him.

But you couldn't keep a baby because of bananas and carrots. If he wasn't yours, you couldn't keep him at all. Wearily, Claire emptied her weekend bag, and refilled it with the emergency kit he'd need if he were to be taken from her at once.

Car after car glided under the darkened trees, and none was *the* car. She was almost relieved when it finally stopped outside her steps and she could open her window to watch the familiar figure leap out with its usual commanding grace.

'Coming right up,' Patrick called, and opened the other door.

And then his passenger was uncoiling into the blue-lit street. Straightening on elegant heels, smoothing the folds of some rich, dark fur, tinkling the gold chain on a gold-framed bag, Donna Cortesi stared up to Claire at the open window with wide, dark, hungry eyes.

CHAPTER NINE

SHE'S smaller than I remembered, Claire thought. And then, What's wrong with me? She's got Patrick, she's come to take Al, and I'm maundering about her *size*?

And yet, there it was. The woman on the pavement below seemed not only smaller but sadder than the Queen of the Night who had claimed homage in the splendour of an embassy.

She's still a queen. Claire noted the tapping foot, the arrogantly raised chin, the dark eyes commanding the circle of blue street-light. But she doesn't rule the stars any more.

She ruled Patrick, though. He didn't take his fascinated gaze from her once during the business of closing the car, and when she hurried to the steps he followed like a courtier.

Or perhaps not a courtier exactly. Claire shut the window and dragged herself to open the door. But, well, he's. . .

Tense was the best word she could find for Patrick's silence. While Donna sailed into the room on a wave of heavy perfume, he gestured Claire back, and closed the door himself without looking either at it or at her. His eyes never left the poised, fur-clad figure of his last love.

Close up, the lustrous fur turned out to be a little rubbed in places. The make-up was perfect, though, and so was the hairstyling—a glossy, blue-black structure of curls which softened the line of the head yet added to its distinction.

'I——' Donna held out a dark-gloved, steel-sprung hand '—am. . . But you know who I am.' As all the

163

peasants do, her tone implied. 'And I,' she pronounced, 'know you.'

'So that's the introductions taken care of.' Could Patrick really be apologising to this—this deposed empress? Perhaps for the modesty of the place which sheltered her royal son? Certainly Donna wasn't bothering to hide her contempt for it. The soot-black eyes flicked from wall to narrow wall.

'Your cell in Tragana is better, no?'

'Er—I don't think. . .' Apart from coping with the rudeness, Claire was having trouble making any sense at all.

She's my height, but that's in heels, with her hair up, her perverse mind was calculating as if it mattered. She must use every trick in the book to seem taller.

She closed her eyes and shook her head, trying to bring her thoughts in order. But the words 'every trick in the book' ticked at her like a bomb, rattled like a. . .

Like a snake. That was it. In spite of the superbly tilted eyes, the perfect cheekbones and raspberry mouth and creamy skin, something about this woman suggested a coiled, dormant. . .

Evil. Claire recalled Daphne's word, and understood it. But that couldn't be right. She was Al's mother, and she'd dropped everything to come and. . .

'Excuse me.'

Donna had almost shouldered her aside in the single short step to the cot. And no, she really couldn't be so bad—look at that smile of incredulous joy.

'So it is here. I could not have believed it.'

'*It*,' Patrick rapped from the door, 'happens to be your son.'

'Fool!'

Donna dropped the insult casually, leaning into the cot. She couldn't mean to lift the baby; you'd never do

that one-handed unless you grabbed an arm or something, and even she wouldn't. . .

Would she? Claire prepared to leap forward, but it
was all right; Donna had picked up the old, blue teddy.

'C-careful with that,' Claire stammered. 'He loves it.'

She'd told Patrick that long ago, in Tragana, before
Al was old enough to know a teddy-bear from a fire-
engine. It had been the least of her lies and yet the worst
in a way, because she'd meant it to hurt. Well, it was
true now, and she was punished.

'Is from Grandpapa.' Donna tore off the once-smart
collar and showed the name tooled into the leather.
'First great-grandson is Alexander, like him.'

Remembering who Grandpapa was, and what had
happened to him, Claire couldn't help shuddering. And
this woman was acting like his true descendant. Dropping the collar without caring where it fell, she peeled
off a glove and probed long, raspberry-red nails into
where the bear's neck would have been if it had one.

Like the gingerbread witch, Clare thought, prodding
Hansel to find out if he's fat enough to eat.

This witch had found whatever she was seeking. For a
fraction of a second she glowed with triumph, then
masked it and turned to where Patrick stood at the door.

'Take me to airport.'

'You're——' Claire stopped herself, refusing to give
in to the wild surge of hope which the words had aroused
in her. 'You're going? Without even holding him?'

'Holding?' The perfect brow furrowed. 'The boy, you
mean?'

'Isn't. . .' it couldn't be as easy as this, it really
couldn't '. . . Isn't that what you came for?'

'I think not.' Patrick stood square and tall before the
closed door. 'Where's that bear, Donna?'

Claire felt her mouth drop open. He was right; the
teddy had vanished.

The glossy head jerked up. 'Is only a nonsense. I think you say, sentimental value. . .'

'Save it.' Patrick stayed blocking the doorway. 'I've been trying to figure what this is all about, ever since I first spoke to you on the phone.'

'Is nothing.' Donna kept one gloved hand at her side, the other hidden in her opulent fur sleeve. 'I wish for souvenir——'

'Stop that!' He advanced on her. 'And let's see it.'

'If you do not wish to take me to airport——'

'You're not going anywhere——' Patrick seemed to fill the tiny space, never releasing the sooty, defiant gaze '—until you give it back.' He stuck out a powerful, upturned palm. 'Give.'

She's certainly brave, Claire thought. I don't know if I could face him if he ever talked like this to me.

But enamelled Donna only drew herself up. 'Never!'

Patrick smiled, coldly but genuinely amused. 'You're not on stage now. Give it back, or I'll take it.'

'And I scream.'

'Wasting your top notes?' This time he laughed aloud. 'So we can tell the police you were stealing our teddy-bear?'

Donna took the point, but faced him undefeated. 'I fight.'

'You'll lose.'

'You hurt lady? You——' the great eyes widened, then half smiled, teasing with some old, shared joke '—English gentleman?'

Patrick's hesitation was of the briefest kind, but Claire caught it. These two had known happier times, you could see that, and now the woman was calling them up for her own reasons, and the man was having to armour himself against the memory of them.

'No, I'd never hurt you.'

'M-Miss Cortesi.' Claire felt low-key, ordinary, an

outsider to this intimate drama. 'We only want Al's bear. H-he loves it.'

The sooty eyes passed her by. They were scanning from Patrick to the door, measuring the distance, calculating the chances. Then they calmed, lengthened, *cozened*.

'You ask, are you father. If I tell, you let me keep?'

Claire gasped, but Donna didn't mean Al. She meant the bear, peeping from the wide sleeve, still captive in those red claws.

Patrick's hand shot out and wrenched. Then he had it, while Donna examined a broken nail and hissed something colourful in her own language. He threw the fluffy thing to Claire, who thrust it instinctively behind her.

'Now we'll bargain.' Still his eyes held Donna's. 'In the kitchen.' He opened the inner door, and switched on the white fluorescent light. 'This needs settling round a table.'

The exiled empress swept by him to arrange her furs on the wooden chair at the head of the plastic kitchen table. Claire instinctively chose the furthest seat away, holding the bear tight with both hands in her lap, and grateful for Patrick's bulk next to her.

'Right, then.' He wasted no time. 'Is he mine, Donna?'

'Is yours. In rehearsals for *Madame Butterfly* I dream.' The red mouth curled in disgust. 'It make me stupid, this rôle.'

'I've been thinking about that. It was the time when you really seemed——' Patrick broke off, staring down at the table. 'Stupid,' he went on at last, expressionless. 'So you forgot to take——'

'I forget nothing, never,' Donna retorted as if to an insult. 'At this time, I think perhaps is good to have child. With you,' she marvelled, 'who are nothing in music and only visitor to my country. This *Butterfly*, this Puccini, they make me stupid.'

'You worked on that rôle from late summer through autumn, and gave birth last May.' Patrick reached to unhook the calendar from the wall, and pointed to November. 'So when you sang *Butterfly* on stage, you were already three months pregnant?'

'Was I not fool?'

'And then, nothing would do but that we go to Paris.' Clearly, he had already worked out this sequence of events. 'I suppose those salon appointments——' he surveyed the mother of his child, stone-faced '—were clinics.'

'If I book operation by letter or phone, Grandpapa know.' Donna took the Cortesi spy system as a fact of life. 'He still find out, from his people in Paris. He send for me, very angry.'

Claire recalled the little parchment-dry old man in the tapestried apartment. Yes, his anger would be frightening.

'To conceive is bad, he say,' Donna continued. 'But to destroy his first great-grandchild, that he will not allow.'

'So he sent you to Tragana.' Claire tried to keep her own voice as cool as Patrick's, but it came out crackly with the horror of what had nearly happened. 'To make sure you didn't. . .'

But she couldn't name it. This was Al they were talking about, who so nearly hadn't been born.

'These stupid Forget-me-nots are with me in the day, in the night,' Donna confirmed. 'But they cannot make me nurse. Once it is over, I never touch.'

She's proud of it, Claire thought, dazed with the effort to understand this alien creature. She sees it as a strength, that she refused to feed her baby.

'So that's why there was plenty of baby-food,' she

murmured aloud. 'What about the baby-alarm? Who fixed it so I'd find Al, after you'd all left?'

'Is Colonel Danev.' Donna granted her a disdainful glance. 'I am with him in night, when orders come.' Her eyes slid to Patrick's, letting him know her meaning. 'We must leave quick, quick, he will not let me go to nursery——'

'So you did want to take Al with you?' Claire interrupted almost in relief.

'Not Al,' Patrick put in drily. 'The bear. I wonder why?'

Donna ignored him. 'He tell me of loudspeaker,' she went on. 'He say nurse wish to take baby to own family in Tragana. . .'

'So Al did have somebody who cared about him!' Claire exclaimed, glad to hear of his unnamed, ordinary woman with ordinary feelings. 'Why didn't she?'

'He say his way better. He wishes his way too much, Colonel Danev,' Donna added viciously. 'Is good I kill him.'

'You. . .' Claire choked to silence.

It was Patrick, much less shocked by this casual boast of murder, who took up the questioning. 'I suppose you did that later, when he couldn't protect you any more?'

'I tell them is revenge for brother. They give me high rank in, how you say——' again that contemptuous curl of the lips '——revolutionary organisation, Students for Freedom. Is useful until I escape. Enough!' The red-nailed hand thrust its demand across the table. 'I have told. Is your turn.'

Claire brought the bear from her lap and slid it slowly, reluctantly away from her. Donna's fingers curved to take it, but Patrick's hand got there first and clamped it where it lay.

The moment seemed to go on forever. Claire studied her own work-worn Sagittarian hand with the short pink nails, and Donna's steely, manicured fingers, and felt grateful for Patrick's great Leo paw separating the two, claiming the battered blue toy.

'You don't need this.' His eyes were obsidian-blue. 'Show whatever's in it, and you can take that.'

Donna's eyes went from Patrick to Claire, down to their motionless hands, back to Patrick. 'You will hold your mouth?'

'You've had the only promise you're getting. And you know I'll keep that.'

'English gentleman!' Half mocking, half admiring, the sooty eyes shifted and calculated. 'Very well. Bring me scissors.'

'You won't damage it too much?' Claire opened the table drawer, glad to move and break the deadlock, dreading the unknown ugliness to come. 'He loves it. . .'

She gave up as the other woman snatched the scissors and ripped the bear's head half from its body. Red shone from the gash like blood, then on Donna's finger, brighter and deeper than the painted nails, a purple-red flare in a diamond rainbow. . .

'The Tragana Flame,' Claire breathed.

'The Devil's Eye,' Patrick murmured.

'Is beautiful, no?' Even Donna sounded impressed. 'And is mine by right. Grandpapa send, to thank for his Alexander.'

Claire remembered the strange little jewel-box made to look like a pack of cards. 'So that was——'

'I don't know about it being yours,' Patrick countered. 'Your grandfather must have taken it from the Malinesis when he took the monastery.'

'Is mine.' Donna coiled to confront him. 'You promise. I fight you for it. . .'

'It's yours.' He dismissed it with a flat, rejecting thrust of that powerful Leo hand.

Claire couldn't help her sigh of relief. Down the

centuries, many had fought for the Tragana Flame, and
none had prospered from it. It was said that Kaspar
Malinesi had cursed it, but human greed was curse
enough for any such prize.

'He send in little box like cards. I sew in toy, is safer.'
Every word of Donna's confirmed the ring's fearsome
reputation. 'Even to sell in secret, will be much money.'

Claire picked up the torn bear, which she must repair
by tomorrow's bedtime. The idea brought her up with a
start.

I'll still have Al. . .but what about Patrick?

He was staring at the blood and rainbow glitter on
Donna's finger. The left-hand middle finger, Claire
noted distantly; the one with the broken nail.

'I'd hide it again, if I were you,' Patrick advised.

'I have glove.' Donna fitted and patted the fine leather
in place, and looked up at him. 'But no English money
for taxi.'

He stood. 'I'd better see you on to the plane.'

She gathered her furs, and swept through the outer
door. While she waited for Patrick to open it, Claire
followed into the soft-lit bed-sitting-room. Could he
really have loved such a woman? Did he maybe love her
still? His face as he opened the door gave nothing away.

Donna didn't bother to say goodbye, or to look back
as she left, but Patrick paused briefly in the doorway.

'We'll sort out the rest of this tomorrow.'

'T-tomorrow?' Claire glanced at her little alarm-clock,
hardly able to believe that it was only nine.

'Try and get some sleep.'

'Sleep!' She shivered in the wind from the open door.

He glanced up at the sparkling umbrellas, whirling
and dancing on their threaded sticks. 'Goodnight,
Claire.'

No promises, no endearments, no warmth. Just that
cold, conventional farewell, and he was gone.

She wouldn't, couldn't open the window to see them drive off. Here was Al's bear to mend before he woke up. She hunted through her cupboards and drawers for cloth to patch it.

'This'll do.'

She clattered the white-gold teething ring to the kitchen table, and cut a piece from the silk scarf which had wrapped it. Then, about to return the ring to its hiding-place, she paused.

'He's no Cortesi. I ought to drop this in the river.'

Hardly knowing what she was doing, she slipped the ring into the inner, zipped pocket of her old, padded jacket, and began her mending. The needle darted through blue fur and sea-green silk, and soon Ted's head was secured to his body by a patch small enough not to worry Al. Claire had just refastened the worn collar when the new, dreadful idea came to her.

Supposing Donna Cortesi comes back? She stared at the red, tooled name of a dead dictator. She'd never get Al, never, but she could make trouble, tell him. . .

Just now it didn't matter. But imagine a little boy starting school—or worse, a gangly, uncertain teen-ager—suddenly assaulted with such knowledge.

I'll have to tell him. But it's got to be at the right time, in whatever way suits him best, Claire decided.

If only Patrick hadn't gone away now, of all times. How could he leave her like this? It could only mean that he still wanted that monster, that serpent-woman who had borne his child. . .

'My child.' She returned the bear to the cot. 'Mine on every record there is. They can't get you, my darling.'

But even the idea of their trying held a pain too deep to face. She pushed it down beneath a grey numbness— the knowledge that, instead of staying here to comfort her, Patrick had bidden her a cold goodnight and gone away with his old love.

Why would he do that—— she slid out of her tweed jacket and skirt—if he didn't have a weakness for her still? She unbound her pulled-back hair, let it fall dark to her waist, and surveyed her image in the glass. Probably he only fancied you because you're a little like her. After all, when he first saw you. . .

Not now, not now; she had this tweed suit to hang up. It seemed forever since she'd worn it to Erlington. As for last night, when she'd taken it off under the sign of the Lion. . .

Not now, not now. She put on her knitted-cotton pyjamas, brushed her hair, cleaned her teeth, and climbed into the narrow, lonely bed which was all she would ever know.

And then they really came at her. Round and round they whirled—grey thoughts like ash in the wind. She'd been in this limbo of unanswered questions ever since she'd first found Al, but Patrick had given the greyness warmth and colour, blown the ash to a glow and fed it to a flame. Where was he now?

Maybe gone to Vienna with Donna Cortesi, she decided miserably. It's just the kind of thing he'd do.

No, no, he couldn't; he needed to agree on some arrangement for Al. That was why he'd promised to return in the morning. He knew he'd never get Al, but then he probably didn't want him any more than Donna wanted him.

He's an honourable man, though, Claire admitted in her limbo of pain. He'll want to help support his son.

With money? The idea was hateful, ugly as the gingerbread witch who was prodding at Al with her long, red nails. . .

'No, witch; no, witch.' She found that she'd spoken it aloud, putting her hand through the blessedly solid bars of the cot to feel the little loved warm mound beneath its blankets. 'You're safe with me, my darling, and I won't ever, ever take any of his horrible, hideous money.'

The decision brought a kind of peace, until the snake-woman invaded her dreams. She had Patrick tangled in her furry folds, her ruby eyes as purple as Al's umbrellas in the dawn light, her hiss turning to a rattle, a clatter, a clunk of milk-bottles on doorsteps and the soft gooing of a contentedly waking baby.

Claire sprang from her bed with relief. Al wasn't used to seeing her this early, but he at once held out his arms. When she picked him up he serenely returned her cuddle, a comforting warmth against that shifting limbo of misery.

'I've still got you.' She settled in the armchair, holding him so that he could dance in her lap. 'That's the most important thing.'

And it was. Long ago, by candle-light in a Tragana mirror, she had seen the perfect family. Painters down the ages had shown it thus, the roundness of the baby doubly shielded by the softness of the woman and the stern darkness of the man. . .

'But you can't have everything,' she told the chuckling baby. 'And I do have you.'

Al was delighted to have got away with an hour less in bed. He accepted the morning routine like an angel, bounced in the swing and threw his teddy about while she dressed, ate all his breakfast, allowed her to bath and dress him, and crowed when she zipped him into his padded suit.

'Yes, walkies now.'

She fought down the longing to stay in for Patrick's return. Let him try at a better time. She had classes this afternoon, so Al must have this outing now, or not at all. She picked him up, settled him on one arm, and opened the door.

'Da!' Al held out his arms. 'Da, da!'

'Wise child.' Patrick stepped inside and took charge of him, of everything, in true Leo style. 'You know your own father.'

He handed Claire the rolled-up newspaper that he was carrying, the better to deal with his lively offspring. Al crowed, and snatched at the absurd little knitted cap which his father had pulled down as usual, pirate-fashion over one eye. Patrick, morning-stubbled as any pirate, fended him off absently.

'You weren't going out, were you?' The eagle-wing eyebrows drew together in displeased enquiry at the sight of her warm sweater and padded jacket. 'I said I'd be back.'

'You didn't say when.' Claire put her hands behind her back so that they wouldn't reach out, newspaper and all, to caress that stubbled jaw, and feel the width of those shoulders in the Aran sweater. 'You can hardly expect us to sit at home all day——'

'Dammit, Claire, this is me, not a man to fix the gas meter.' He let Al pull his cap off, and faced her with his hair roughed to a lion's mane. 'We've a lot to talk about.'

She fielded the cap as Al threw it. 'It'll keep.'

'It'll what? Are you out of your mind?' He blocked her exit and Al waved his fists, a solidarity of fighting Donovans.

'It was all right for you to go away and leave me last night——' she couldn't meet his eyes '—but this morning when I——'

'Last night, I had to go.' He advanced into the room while the sparkly umbrellas danced in the wind from the door. 'Did you expect me to let her find her own way to the airport, with a fortune on her finger?'

'She's not exactly a virgin with a pot of gold on her head,' Claire retorted. 'I'd say that horrible ring was safer with her than it would be with Securicor.'

'Maybe it would have been. . .' He stopped, the dark blue eyes sombre. 'That's one of the things I've got to. . .' But he had to stop again, as Al's fist made contact with his temple. 'Look, this is impossible.' He held on to the fist, ignoring Al's protest. 'We can't talk until we've dropped him off.'

'My mother's got classes all morning,' Claire said quickly, glad it was true. 'Besides, what's to talk about?'

Did he want to tell her that he'd decided to take up again with Donna Cortesi? Because if so, good luck and good riddance, and she didn't want to hear about it now or ever.

'I don't want a penny from you,' she added, firm in last night's resolve. 'And if you're going to be with that. . .' she swallowed the several words she might have used '. . .with *her*, then I'm not sure I even want you visiting. What are you doing?'

He didn't answer, just pushed her out of the wide-open door. She had to grab the iron rail and get down the steps any way she could with the two Donovans crowding after. And, in the street, when he opened his car there seemed no way but to get into it and wait there while he fitted Al into the baby-seat at the back.

'Where are we going?' she asked. 'I won't be——'

'Shut up.'

'Gur, da,' Al egged him on from the back.

And that was all she could get from either of them until they reached the Wandsworth street where Daphne and her husband had bought a house. Daphne, now visibly pregnant, was out of her door and on to the pavement before Claire could do more than lower her window.

'Isn't this marvellous? I do hope you——'

'Da, da.' Al, lifted from the baby-seat by Patrick, wrapped his arms round her neck.

'The clever darling knows my name!' She hugged him.

'I'm sure you helped me get my baby, Alexander Fletcher.'

'Till lunchtime.' Patrick was already starting the car.

'Till then,' she agreed, and gently waved Al's arm for him. 'Say goodbye to Mummy, darling.'

And they glided away under spring-budding trees, round parked cars, and into another drive in the same street.

'What is all this?' Claire looked up at the solid Victorian house of beautiful weathered rosy brick. 'Why. . .'

'Out.' Already he had her door open.

He led her through a door with stained-glass panels, into a deep-carpeted hall. She just had time to note the wide stairway before his hand on her arm propelled her into a room facing the street and full of fretted Turkish-style furniture.

'Sit.' He pointed to a couch. 'I've something bad to tell.'

She stayed on her feet. 'I can hear it standing up——'

'Sit, I said!'

The Lion-roar would not be denied, even by the Archer. She glanced down at the low, floppy couch, and perched instead on a carved chair. He made sure that she was really in it, then held out a hand. She found to her fury that she was still clutching his cap and his newspaper. She wanted to throw them at him Al-style, but already he'd taken the paper from her, opened it to its tabloid front page, and partly displayed it.

She refused to look. 'You surely didn't buy this trash?'

'Forget your snobbery, and read that headline.'

In spite of her desire to disobey, she could hardly avoid it. CORTESI'S GRANDDAUGHTER STABBED. . . Claire caught her breath, and tried to snatch the paper, but he tossed it to the floor face down. When she leaned to pick it up, he put a foot on it and pushed her back in her chair.

'I'm not involved; it was at Vienna airport,' he answered her unspoken question. 'You're not looking at that picture, though. They shouldn't publish such things.'

'You mean it shows. . .' She choked, her mind echoing kapitan Todoresi's comment:

'*Very quick, much blood, no bullets,*' he'd said, and, '*Many kill so, for blood-feud.*'

'Wh-who did it?' she asked at last.

'Colonel Danev's son.' His voice reflected his distaste. 'He says she acted like a man when she killed his father, so——'

'Patrick——' she sprang up in terror '—will they come for Al? They never spare males, however young. . .'

And then those strong arms were around her, and she could hide in the cabled wool over that broad chest.

'Relax, my darling; Michael Danev's in custody.' He stroked her back, down her spine and up to her shoulder-blades, down and up, down and up. 'Besides, Al's ours.'

'Ours?' She pulled away. 'The Leo royal "we"?'

'The Donovan we. You and me.'

'It would have to be, wouldn't it?' She held away, last night's misery too vivid to forget. 'I'm the one who's left.'

'The one's who's——' He broke off to stare at her. 'You can't really believe. . . There, there.' He patted her shoulder. 'It's all been too much for you,' he assured her with lofty Leo wisdom. 'You'll be better soon.'

'I'm fine,' she snapped, nettled by his humouring tone. 'And if you don't love her now, you must have once.'

'Yes, we loved each other once.' The dark blue eyes met hers, sober and sincere. 'That's what she called being——' his mouth tightened in pain and distaste

'—*stupid*. Do you really think I'd prefer a woman like that to you?'

'But yesterday, when you knew you were going to see her, you *sang* about her.'

'I did what?'

'You were singing "She's my girl."'

'What on earth. . .?' He listened to the tune she was humming. 'That's "He's my guy."'

'Yes, but when it's a girl. . .'

'What girl? Al's a boy. *My* boy.'

'Oh.' Observing his pride in his son, she felt foolish at her own mistake. 'So you really, really never wanted Donna back?'

'For heaven's sake, Claire, you saw how she. . .' He glanced at the crumpled paper at their feet. 'Let her rest.'

'You were so cold, last night, when you went away with her.'

'She. . .she made me go cold inside,' he confessed, reluctant to admit this foolishness of his own. 'I couldn't help seeing her as a witch, who'd put a curse on us if we gave the least sign. . .'

'I do love you, Patrick.' She had to cling to him then, unable to put into words her delight that his thoughts should have been so like her own.

'You told me that already,' he countered, aggrieved, 'but you haven't said you'll marry me yet.'

'Haven't I?' She nestled on his shoulder, his stubbled jaw against her hair. 'Why didn't you shave this morning?'

'I had to get to you fast. For lots of good reasons, but mostly because I just wanted to.'

'And what are we doing in this entirely strange house?'

'Ah. Yes.' He opened the door wide. 'I've rented it, with an option to buy.'

'So that's why Daphne's so pleased. She thinks we're going to be neighbours, and I'm supposed to——' Claire broke off, kicking uselessly in his arms. 'What are you doing?'

'I should have carried you over the threshold.' He swept her through the door and up the stairs. 'This is instead.'

The bed he set her on was huge—a modern four-poster. Its filmy curtains were drawn back to show a blaze of yellow and black zebra-striped duvet and pillows. While she sank into it, wriggling and laughing and protesting, he flicked at the grip which kept her hair out of the way. The heavy swathes slid down her neck, helped by his greedy, gentle, fire-raising fingers until it ran smoothly down her shoulders and back.

'Now, Claire Fletcher. Will you be Claire Donovan, or do I have to kidnap you?'

'You seem to have done that anyway,' she teased, dodging his possessing arms and rolling quickly to the other side of the bed.

He grabbed the hem of her coat, but she slid out of it. As he held it upside-down, a glint of gold dropped from its pocket to the duvet. Patrick picked it up and examined it.

'So this is the famous teething-ring.'

She shivered in the warm room. 'I was going to take it to Tower Bridge, and drop it in the Thames.'

'Silly.' He smiled lovingly across the bed, the ring in his strong grip. 'I see it has space for us to put in the Donovan.'

'Why, of course!' The last of her superstitious fears melted and vanished. 'He's Alexander *Donovan*, really. Nothing to do with that other foul ring.' Made brave by his loving presence, she could even speculate. 'I wonder what's become of it now?'

'The Devil's Eye?'

'The Tragana Flame.'

'Who cares?' He set the teething-ring carefully on the bedside-table. 'Now, are you going to be sensible, and marry me?'

'I'm not sure that's sensible at all.' She looked down at the zebra-striped duvet. 'Who chose this?'

'I did.'

'There'll have to be changes.'

'Make them.'

'I could, couldn't I?' She spoke wonderingly, realising her power. 'Starting right now.'

And before she could give herself time to think about it, her sweater was up over her head. On the floor by her feet it was quickly joined by her trousers, and by the scraps of lace she no longer needed to hide her pert breasts and flat belly. When she faced him, her instinct was to cover herself with her hands, but she resisted it, and shook her long hair back out of the way.

'In the Lion,' she offered timidly, 'you wanted to see me.'

'Don't I just!' He almost whispered it. 'Remember how I took you for Donna?'

She nodded, hanging her head. 'That's one reason. . . I mean, back in Tragana, I was just a substitute. . .'

'No.' He stretched a hand to her across the bed. 'I fell for Donna because she looked a little like you.'

'But that doesn't make sense.' All the same, she placed her hand in his. 'You didn't even know me.'

She might as well have argued with his starry Leo, except that was cold and far, and he was hot and here. He tugged gently, pulling her to the bed.

'I knew you.'

And then it all happened. First the zebra-striped duvet somehow tangled with them—her long hair and his Aran sweater, her arms and his, and striped padding and pillows sliding about and popping up in crazy

places. Then all the stripes were on the floor, and so
were his clothes, and their bodies were free to meet at
last with nothing between them. To meet, mingle, rise
together like flames from tinder, soar together with the
strength of the lion, the speed of the arrow, to some
distant, dazzling world where Lion and Archer dissolved
in flame and dropped gently, gently back to a wide
zebra-striped sheet.

'I didn't know it was going to be like that,' she
murmured when she could talk again. 'I mean, I
knew—well, I hoped—it wouldn't hurt any more,
but——'

'It's never been like that for me before, either.' He
took her left hand, kissed the palm, played with the
fingers, then sat up sharply and slapped his own forehead. 'There, look what you've made me forget!'

'Oh, it's my fault, is it?' She propped herself on one
elbow and laughed as he reached down to his clothes,
still tangled with the striped duvet on the floor. 'I
suppose I might as well get used to it. . . What's this?'

'A little something.' Patrick dropped the tiny box back
on to the floor, and showed her the silver and turquoise
eternity-ring. 'Let's be having that hand.'

'The Saggittarius stone.' She stared at the blue-green,
endless circle. 'When did you buy it?'

'Two months ago. For my list.' He slid the ring on to
the third finger of her left hand. 'It's nearly finished
now.'

'Nearly?' She held the ring to admire, then stroked it
lovingly through that early-morning stubble. 'What
else?'

'Nothing much. Just a little matter of a marriage to be
arranged.' He turned his head and pretended to bite her
finger. 'The wedding-ring, and the engagement-ring. I
can't afford a ruby like the Tragana Flame, but——'

'Don't!' She had to rub her cheek against him, to feel

the cleansing roughness and the sheltering strength of her beloved Lion. 'My Tragana Flame's where it's always been.'

'And mine, my darling.' He drew her to him. 'And mine.'

STARGAZING

YOUR STAR SIGN: **LEO (July 24–August 23)**

LEO is the fifth sign of the Zodiac, ruled by the Sun and controlled by the element of Fire. These make you proud, exuberant and generous and sometimes arrogant. Your strong sense of power, courage and vanity make you king of the jungle: beware, anyone who tries to defy you! But those who get close to you discover that you're really a pussy cat underneath that hard exterior!

Socially, Leos love fun and games—you possess a lively sense of humour and can roar with laughter as long as the jokes are not made at your expense. At home you are likely to be leader of the pack and enjoy lavishing money to create a warm and secure environment.

Your characteristics in love: Passionate, caring and affectionate, Leos love being in love and will do anything to gain their partners' attention and admiration. Nevertheless, once you are adored, you are a very faithful partner and can be quite sensitive even if you hate to admit it. For the Leo woman, relationships can be quite difficult, as you insist on getting your own way; being so defiant and demanding, you won't settle for second fiddle. Therefore you are more likely to opt for partners who can fuel your passionate fire and who look after you well.

Star signs which are compatible with you: Sagittarius, **Aries**, **Gemini** and **Libra**, while **Aquarius**, **Taurus** and **Scorpio** provide you with a challenge. Partners born under other signs can be compatible, depending on which planets reside in their Houses of Personality and Romance.

What is your star-career? Leos take great pride in their work and enjoy constant recognition for their creative talents. A distinctive regal style coupled with self-confidence drives Leos to the top of the career ladder. Positions which need individuality, flair and being in the limelight will appeal to you, such as management, sport, fashion, film work, and teaching.

Your colours and birthstones: Rich, opulent colours such as gold and deep yellows will match your sunny personality. Your birthstones are ruby and amber; they are said to protect the wearer from aches and pains such as headaches. Rubies—also known as 'drops of blood from Mother Earth's heart'—are thought to have healing powers for diseases of the blood. Amber—a yellow stone—is said to encourage virility and fertility.

LEO ASTRO-FACTFILE

Day of the week: Sunday
Countries: Italy and Morocco.
Flowers: Daffodil, sunflower, marigold and camomile.
Food: Oranges, lemons, fillet steak and pumpkins; Leos enjoy entertaining in great style by planning special celebrations and throwing elaborate dinner parties—so long as they are seated at the head of the table!
Health: Be careful not to go over-board with all that passion and drive in an effort to impress others—you'll have to face up to your mortality sooner of later! Ease up a little and you'll feel much better at the end of the day.

You share your star sign with these famous names:

Whitney Houston	Robert de Niro
Robert Redford	Yves Saint-Laurent
Jacqueline Kennedy	the Queen Mother
Ray Bradbury	Dustin Hoffman
Mick Jagger	Madonna
Roman Polanski	Daley Thompson

ZODIAC LOVE MATCH

CALL THE MILLS & BOON
LOVE MATCH HOTLINE

The only service to give you a detailed love analysis of your own star sign and then tell you how romantically compatible you are with the man of your dreams.

If you're interested in hearing how you match up with that special man in your life, or just want to know who would suit you best, all you have to know is your own star sign and that of the man you're interested in hearing yourself matched with.

If you dial the special Love Match 'phone number shown below, we will connect you to Catriona Roberts Wright who will give you an in-depth report on how compatible your two signs are.

CAN YOU BEAR TO WAIT?

Mills & Boon

Accept 4 Free Romances and 2 Free gifts

•FROM READER SERVICE•

An irresistible invitation from
Mills & Boon Reader Service.
Please accept our offer of 4 free
Romances, a CUDDLY TEDDY and a
special MYSTERY GIFT... Then, if you
choose, go on to enjoy 6 captivating
Romances every month for just £1.60
each, postage and packing free. Plus our
FREE newsletter with author news,
competitions and much more.

Send the coupon below to:
Reader Service, FREEPOST, PO Box 236,
Croydon, Surrey CR9 9EL.

------------ NO STAMP REQUIRED ------------

Yes! Please rush me my 4 free Romances and 2 free gifts! Please also
reserve me a Reader Service Subscription. If I decide to subscribe I can
look forward to receiving 6 new Romances each month for just £9.60,
postage and packing is free. If I choose not to subscribe I shall write to you
within 10 days - I can keep the books and gifts whatever I decide. I may
cancel or suspend my subscription at any time. I am over 18 of age.

Name Mrs/Miss/Ms/Mr _____ EP17R

Address _____

_____

Postcode _____ Signature _____

Offer expires 31st May 1992. The right is reserved to refuse an application
and change the terms of this offer. Readers overseas and in Eire please send
for details. Southern Africa write to Independant Book Services, Postbag
X3010, Randburg 2125. You may be mailed with offers from other reputable
companies as a result of this application.

If you would prefer not to share in this opportunity, please tick box ☐

Next month's Romances

Each month, you can choose from a world of variety in romance with Mills & Boon. These are the new titles to look out for next month.

A FIERY BAPTISM Lynne Graham

A TIME TO DREAM Penny Jordan

SLEEPING PARTNERS Charlotte Lamb

RUNAWAY FROM LOVE Jessica Steele

DARK CAPTOR Lindsay Armstrong

DARK AND DANGEROUS Mary Lyons

AN UNFINISHED AFFAIR Jenny Arden

THE GYPSY'S BRIDE Rosalie Ash

ISLAND INTERLUDE Anne McAllister

RIDE A STORM Quinn Wilder

AN EARLY ENCHANTMENT Stephanie Wyatt

A MATTER OF HONOUR Stephanie Howard

LOVE'S DOUBLE FOOL Alison York

RIGHT CONCLUSIONS Helena Dawson

ICE LADY Emma Goldrick

STARSIGN
ON GOSSAMER WINGS Shirley Kemp

Available from Boots, Martins, John Menzies, W.H. Smith, Woolworths and other paperback stockists.

Also available from Mills and Boon Reader Service, P.O. Box 236, Thornton Road, Croydon, Surrey CR9 3RU.